SIMULATION OF THE URBAN ENVIRONMENT

by

Barry M. Kibel

Department of City and Regional Planning
University of North Carolina

ASSOCIATION OF AMERICAN GEOGRAPHERS
Commission on College Geography
Washington, D.C. 20009

TECHNICAL PAPER NO. 5

Library of Congress Catalog Card Number 78-185555

Supported by a grant from the National Science Foundation

FOREWORD

The Technical Papers are explanatory manuals for the use of both instructors and students. They are expository presentations of available information on each subject designed to encourage innovation in teaching methods and materials. These Technical Papers are developed, printed, and distributed by the Commission on College Geography under the auspices of the Association of American Geographers with National Science Foundation support. The ideas presented in these papers do not necessarily imply endorsement by the AAG. Single copies are mailed free of charge to all AAG members.

John F. Lounsbury
Project Director
Commission on College Geography

Paul W. English
Chairman, Panel on Resource
and Technical Papers

Panel Members

Ian Burton, University of Toronto
Paul W. English, University of Texas
Leslie J. King, McMaster University
Harold M. Rose, University of Wisconsin, Milwaukee
Robert H. T. Smith, Queen's University
Edward W. Soja, Northwestern University
Philip L. Wagner, Simon Fraser University

CONTENTS

Preface

PREFACE

This Technical Paper has been written specifically for use by students and instructors in undergraduate geography programs. Its objective is to introduce the readers to the field of urban simulation and to provide materials for utilizing simulation models within geography curricula. It is assumed that this Paper represents the first comprehensive introduction to this technical area for the readers.

The author of this Paper considers himself to be an urbanist, not a geographer. Accordingly the orientation will not be limited to the usual sets of problems and issues covered in geography courses, but will cut across other related disciplines as well: most notably, economics, sociology, political science, and city planning. Consequently, this work may be of interest to a broader set of readers than its target group.

Furthermore, while the target group are professors and students operating at the college undergraduate level, the materials covered in this Paper may well be of use in graduate level education and research, on the one hand, and in high school and grade school classwork, on the other.

Some of the materials contained in this Paper have been drawn from the author's Ph.D. dissertation, *Gaming Simulation of Urban Spatial Processes*. Other materials have developed as a product of classes and seminars later conducted by the author at Howard University. The following individuals and groups have all made substantive contributions to this work in its formulative stages: Richard Meier, Allan Pred, John Nystuen, Riki Kibel, Richard Snyder and students at the University of California at Berkeley and Howard University in Washington, D.C.

One final note. The literature on simulation and gaming is rich and rapidly growing. The field may be approached from many vantage points. My personal entry was through military field simulation, urban planning, geography, and learning theory. My biases are scattered throughout the following text. My attitudes toward urban simulation are very personal ones. The interested reader will quickly discover a range of alternative uses for, and attitudes toward, simulation models. Serious pursuit of the subject matter should eventually lead one to his own personal style and biases.

Barry Kibel
August 1971

CHAPTER ONE

THE NATURE OF THE URBAN ENVIRONMENT

Definition of the Urban Environment

When one speaks about the "city" or an "urban area," what in fact is being referred to? An expanse of land containing people and structures? A communications network connecting places of residence with places of work, trade, and play? A crowded mass of individuals and family units gathered together for survival and, when that is assured, for increased pleasures (however that may be defined)? A non-agriculturally based economy and complementary social network? A politically and administratively defined activity space?

No doubt when one speaks about the "city" or an "urban area," all of the above are meant, at least to some degree. In developing a composite, all-encompassing definition of the "urban environment," it is therefore necessary to include all the above-mentioned elements. Consider the following "partial definitions":

1. An urban environment, as *economically* defined, is a system of major and minor markets and production points engaged in the creation; receipt; and/or transfer of goods and services both internally (within the boundaries of the environment, however delineated) and externally; for the support and profit of participants operating within the system.
2. An urban environment, as *socially* defined, is a system of culturally-related institutions and groupings designed to permit interaction and interchange among individuals; with the quest of knowledge, experiences, entertainment, and other satisfactions as the motivating dynamic.
3. An urban environment, as *politically* defined, is a system for exercising the public will through the actions and transactions among designated representatives.
4. An urban environment, as *administratively* defined, is a system for managing public affairs and for providing public goods (example: roads) and public services (example: education).
5. An urban environment, as *spatially* defined, is a boundary-specific area encompassing interrelated economic, social, political and administrative systems; and shaped and contained within natural barriers (example: moutains) and man-made barriers (example: political jurisdictions).
6. An urban environment, as *structurally* defined, is a dense composite of buildings, spaces, networks of communication, and other natural and man-made focal points; which together present a three-dimensional panorama.

1

What then is an urban environment? An *urban environment* is a dynamic, changing spatially and structurally defined set of economic, social, political, and administrative systems acting concurrently and interdependently to meet real and perceived needs of its residents and other users. Such an environment may be called "neighborhood," "city," "metropolis," "region," "nation," or even "world" depending on one's orientation or level of inquiry.

This definition—or rather assemblage of partial definitions—is meant to be illustrative, rather than definitive. The reader is welcome to disagree with any portion of it. This should not significantly impede free interaction with the materials which follow. What is important here is that the reader be willing to accept a broad-based notion of the urban environment, so that the richness of what follows can be more fully gleaned.

Characteristics of the Urban Environment

Given this rather elaborate definition of the urban environment, what are those characteristics of particular importance to an investigation of it? That is, which properties, when taken together, portray the essential nature of the urban environment; and, when examined separately, provide necessary insights into one's understanding of this environment? Consider the following set of properties:

1. *The urban environment has both spatial (locational) and non-spatial (location-free) components.* Certain urban activities are location specific: "I am going to the stadium to see the Mets play the Cubs." Other urban activities are less locked to some specified location or locations: "I will vote for Smith for Mayor." However, what should be made clear is that no urban activity is devoid of either spatial or non-spatial elements. "I am going to the stadium," while essentially a description of movement from my current location to some clearly defined site elsewhere in the area, contains a long list of basically non-spatial repercussions, such as purchasing a ticket, enjoying myself, eating a hotdog, etc. Similarly, "I will vote for Smith for Mayor" implicitly—if not explicitly, depending on Smith's platform—contains a number of forthcoming spatial repercussions, such as the ultimate location of the controversial northeast freeway, the new site for the stadium, or a revitalized downtown area.

   What is being suggested here is that an urban activity is *never* an isolated event. There are always repercussions and implications associated with a given activity. And these will always include both spatial and non-spatial consequences. Yet, the property itself (spatial versus non-spatial) is still a useful one, in that it provides a convenient and often worthwhile system for classification and aggregation of activities and events. However, what must be kept in the fore are the non-spatial as well as spatial consequences of essentially spatial activities; and conversely, the spatial as well as non-spatial consequences of essentially non-spatial activities.

2. *The urban environment is a highly interdependent social system.* This impossibility of totally segregating any urban event from the wealth of

2

related and indirect spatial and non-spatial repercussions demonstrates the interdependency of all urban activities. Decisions or actions focusing on one or more parts of the urban environment have repercussions extending in varying ways and to various degrees to all other parts of the environment. For example, a decision to locate a new university campus in an isolated corner of an urban area will ultimately mean a reorientation of the entire traffic system of the area, as a result of new student and faculty populations, new life styles, new activities related to the campus, shifts to new locations of older establishments, and the like. Or, for example, a proposed manpower program designed to train the so-called "hard-core" unemployed for jobs in the area, will require changes in the delivery of services usually not associated with job training *per se* to be successful. These might include changes in health services, transportation services, child care services, family counseling services, financial services, and the like.

Is it really possible to trace through an urban activity to include all direct and indirect repercussions? Obviously not. Any attempt to do this would be "mind-boggling" at best. Analytical—and educational—decisions will have to be made concerning where to draw the line, where to give up the quest for more repercussions, for more interactions.

3. *The richness of alternatives within the urban environment, coupled with limitations on most resources, requires that trade-offs be made continually.* Human resources are limited. Only a finite number of projects (social or economic ventures) can be undertaken, despite the endless variety of candidate projects. Monetary resources are also limited. There is never enough accumulated capital to support all worthwhile projects. Consequently, priorities must be established and allocation decisions made with the realization that any action taken results in the immediate loss of other opportunities. For example, if the last dollar is spent for education, it cannot be spent for health. If the last hour of professional time is spent working on a project in neighborhood one, it cannot be spent on the project in neighborhood two.

The importance of this property becomes increasingly clear when one examines the dynamics underlying the economic system, the social system, and/or the political system. In any of these, trade-offs are constantly being made as the participants, individually and collectively, seek out profitable positions, as measured by their wealth, status, power, or self-respect. By viewing the urban environment as a "decision-space" involving the allocation of limited resources for the achievement of political, economic, social and psychological profitability, keen insights may often emerge.

4. *The urban environment is composed of highly behavioral systems of activities.* The forces at work in our urban areas are largely the products of human decisions. The bulk of these decisions is made independently by individuals exercising their free will. However, the latitude and diversity of these "private decisions" is largely determined by a much smaller number of

3

public and private decisions made by the economic, social, and political leaders of our society. These latter decisions have been referred to in the literature as "priming decisions," because of the analogy with priming of a pump (where a small amount of water introduced externally permits the flow of water from the pump to begin) or with priming of an explosion (by setting off a small charge, the entire explosive force is unleashed). The multitude of resulting private decisions are thus referred to as "secondary decisions."

To fully grasp the complexities of the urban environment, it is necessary to understand both the motivations and "rules" underlying these priming decisions and the resultant flows of secondary decisions emerging from them. Thus, for example, the freeway location decision must be examined from the perspective of the politicians, "community leaders," and technicians advocating a given plan and from that of the residences, businesses, and institutions immediately and indirectly affected by the plan, if enacted. Of growing interest in our current decade of political confrontation, is the manner in which so-called "secondary actors" can collectively influence the decisions of "priming actors."

5. *The urban environment can be viewed as sets of predictable dramas being enacted simultaneously at different social, economic, and political levels.* Economic, social and political processes within the urban environment consist largely of transactions among individuals and groups of individuals. Economic transactions involve the exchange of material resources. Social transactions involve the exchange of status, satisfaction, and knowledge. Political transactions involve the exchange of power. The protocol (rules and ethics) governing these various transactions tend to channel individuals and groups into very stereotypical roles. Thus, the average individual engaged in buying groceries at a supermarket behaves a certain predictable way. The average corporate business meeting concerning reorganization of departments follows a predictable pattern. Obviously, variations and surprises exist. Without these, the urban environment—and human life itself—would be rather drab and automatic. However, there are sufficient similarities among the bulk of urban transactions to permit useful generalizations to be drawn.

6. *The urban environment is in continual flux.* Individual and group decisions result in the decay, abandonment, or disappearance of physical, social, and economic units; and in the birth or development of new units. These births and deaths are often of a collective nature; thus, whole neighborhoods decay and undergo shifts in character or functional use, other neighborhoods are created in formerly vacant hinterlands.

In this manner, the urban environment undergoes continual transformation, adapting to new technologies, human aspirations and societal values. Through investigation of the dynamics of change, one begins to gain deep insights into the character of the urban environment. It is at the points of change that the underlying structure of the environment is most clearly exposed.

Synthesis

The urban environment, then, is indeed complex. It is an ever-changing, highly behavioral "super system" of spatial and non-spatial forces. Included within this "super system" are economic, social, political, and administrative systems—all interrelated and interdependent. At the core of each of these systems are human decision-makers, acting individually and in formal and informal groupings.

Yet, the urban environment can be comprehended and dealt with despite this complexity. The natural environment, within which an urban environment functions, provides specific exploitable resources as well as water and terrain barriers with varying degrees of "conquerability," each of which determine the shape and character of the urban environment. Furthermore, the "rules" and "ethics" underlying the economic, social, political and administrative systems are sufficiently well-defined and enforced throughout a given culture to insure broad similarities within that culture. Finally, the human character, when viewed collectively, is usually quite predictable. Individual variations tend to balance within the various systems to produce generalizable trends and behavior patterns.

Thus, the real trick is not so much producing an overall working model of the urban environment (for purposes of understanding, research, education, or professional endeavors) which conforms with real world patterns. This is not very difficult, considering the regularities as explained just above. What is difficult is to produce a working model which provides insights as to the workings of the urban environment whether the "super system," the systems, or sub-systems within these systems are the subjects of analysis and/or inquiry. A model which continues to provide useful insights at all the working levels of the urban environment is what should be sought.

The purpose of this Paper is to show how simulation techniques may be utilized for building the foundations for such a working model of the urban environment.

CHAPTER TWO

URBAN SPATIAL PROCESSES

"... to see not only the *causes* acting on the phenomena under study, the possible *consequences* of the phenomena, and the possible *mutual interactions* of some of these factors, but also to see the *total emergent processes* as a function of possible positive and/or negative *feedbacks* mediated by the *selective decisions,* or "choices," of the individuals and groups directly or indirectly involved. No less complex an approach can be expected to get at the complexity of the phenomena studied."

Walter Buckley, 1967.

In this chapter, the spatial dynamics of the urban environment are examined. An attempt will be made to explain in systemic terms how the urban environment is shaped and reshaped by social, economic, political—and natural—forces. In later chapters, various aspects of this formulation of urban spatial processes will be explored through the use of simulation techniques. In this manner, it is hoped that the reader will gain an awareness and appreciation of the richness of simulation in illustrating and explaining how the urban environment functions.

Spatial Diffusion

Assume that in 1940 an aerial photograph was made which included the actual location of every structure within a given urban area. Assume further that this procedure was repeated annually through 1971, so that today a set of 32 such photographs of the area exist. With the use of old telephone books or public records it would be possible to identify the use or uses of each structure (residence, barber shop, women's shoe store, hotel, etc.) and so label them on the various photographs.

Now suppose that a given activity were selected—say women's dress shops—and color-coded on the 32 maps for easy identification. If any two successive maps were selected (that is, maps depicting two consecutive years), some new dress shop locations might have appeared and a few old locations might have been abandoned; but the overall spatial patterns for dress shops in the two time periods would be very similar. However, if a comparison were made of two spatial plots of dress shop locations several years apart (say 1943 and 1967), a relatively large number of new locations ("births") should likely have appeared, and a number of old locations will have probably been abandoned ("deaths"). Moreover, a shift in the overall spatial pattern of dress shops between the two time periods will most likely be detected.

7

If these aerial photographs containing the color-coded dress shop locations were piled chronologically, a rapid flipping of this pile would produce a cartoon-like effect. The shifting dress shop locations would be reminiscent of high school biology days, when the growth cycle of the amoebas was studied. Clusters of dress shop locations would be seen forming, shifting, and splitting off into smaller clusters; which in turn grew and subdivided or disappeared. This amoeba-like growth pattern would reassert itself for most social or economic activities which were studied in the same manner as the dress shops.

These "births" and "deaths" of a given social or economic activity are the direct consequence of individual decision-making units (individual households, business-men, corporations, land developers, etc.) exercising their options within the urban environment. Such an on-going process of births and deaths of a given activity type, resulting in amoeba-like shifts in overall spatial distribution over time, is referred to as a *spatial diffusive process.*

Each spatial diffusion process is governed by a unique set of "laws." These "laws," in turn, are derived as a composite of behavioral rules of the individual decision-making units within the given activity type. Thus, for example, the dress shop locations in a city tend as a group to cluster along major streets and particularly in downtown retail and business districts, outlying shopping centers, and near middle and upper income residential areas. Individual dress shop owners consider factors such as trip patterns of their target clientele, location of competitors, and general atmosphere of the surrounding area. Collectively these individual decision rules give rise to the clustering pattern described above.

Complementary and Repelling Processes

Let us assume that an analysis over time had just been completed for women's dress shop locations utilizing the aerial photograph plotting technique described earlier. Would it be necessary to repeat a similar analysis to identify the spatial diffusion pattern for women's shoe stores? No, it would not. Once we are familiar with the pattern for women's dress shops, we immediately know the general pattern for women's shoe stores. They are nearly identical.

The reason for this is simple. The same general "laws" which govern the location of women's dress shops hold true as well for women's shoe stores. That is, the decision rules for the individual decision-making units are virtually identical. Furthermore, when an individual is planning a new location for a women's shoe store one of his major considerations will be to locate nearby women's dress shops. When a woman buys a new dress, she is likely to want new shoes. Thus, these two spatial processes are highly *complementary.* Other examples of complementary processes would include supermarkets and middle income housing; bus stations and "dirty" book stores; major road intersections and gasoline stations.

On the other hand, certain processes may be strongly related—but in a negative fashion. That is, the "birth" of one or more units of a given activity signals the forthcoming "death" of one or more units of another activity type. Thus, for example, the spatial diffusion process depicting white, middle-class residences in the 1950's and 1960's was frequently negatively related to the spatial diffusion process depicting black, middle-class residences. The entrance of black families into an area quickly led to the outflow of white families. This in turn created vacancies which only additional black families were willing to fill, driving out still more white families. In this manner, an all-white area soon became an all-black area. Thus, these two spatial processes are *highly repelling* rather than complementary.

Other examples of repelling processes would include heavy traffic generators and schools; factories and department stores; public housing projects and single family middle-income dwellings.

The urban environment as a whole, therefore, can be characterized as containing a multitude of spatial diffusion processes, some of which are complementary and others of which are repelling. But what gives the environment its shape? That is, how do these processes arrange themselves in space?

Spatial Barriers

Present in the urban environment are a multitude of barriers which impede the spread of selected spatial diffusion processes. These barriers may be natural, man-made, legal, institutionalized, or social-psychological. The results are the same: The direction of spread ("births" of new locations) of some or all activities is altered. (Figure 1).

Consider a city located along the seacoast. The sea acts as a *permanent natural barrier,* preventing the flow of any land-oriented activity in that direction. Thus activities can only spread in the other three directions. However, consider a city developed in a valley. As the city grows and spreads, certain activities eventually begin to work their way up the sides of the surrounding hills, others do not. Thus, the hills act as a barrier to certain activities, but not to others.

For example, consider the complementary spatial diffusion processes of

Figure 1

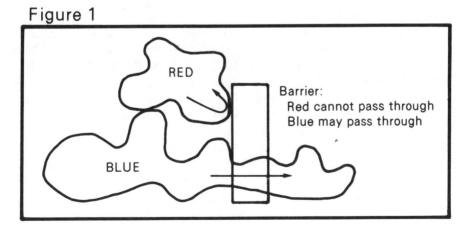

BLUE

RED

Barrier:
Red cannot pass through
Blue may pass through

middle-income housing and supermarkets. As the housing spreads, new super-markets appear to serve the newly located housing. These supermarkets tend to space themselves in such a way that each has a clearly defined primary neighborhood to serve. However, upon reaching a hillside, the middle income housing begins to work its way upward along the winding roads. The flow of supermarkets however is impeded, and the result is often a clustering of several supermarkets at major intersections at the foot of the hill. Thus, the hillside has acted as a *natural discriminating barrier.*

Not all natural barriers are permanent. A water barrier (say, a bay), may initially serve to stop the spread of activities. But, as increased demand for land is expressed, a decision is made to fill some of the shallower areas to provide additional land for development. (Note: through such a process, the San Francisco Bay has been shrunk to virtually half its original dimensions). Thus, what was once a "permanent" barrier has in fact proven to be a *temporary natural barrier* which gives way to technology and "progress." Other examples of temporary natural barriers would be rivers (which impede activity spread until bridges are built across them) and wooded areas (which impede activity spread until they are cleared).

Most barriers in the urban environment, however, are not natural. They are man-made. Accordingly, they are never permanent but rather are altered or eliminated as a result of changing conditions. A zoning ordinance, for example, essentially puts up sets of *man-made discriminating barriers* throughout the area which dictate which activities may pass through and continue their regular spread and which activities must be turned back and forced to spread elsewhere.

A land speculator buys up land and holds it until the demand is such that he reaps a high rate of return on his investment. In the meantime, this "frozen" land serves as a *temporary man-made barrier* interfering with the natural social and economic forces of growth.

Certain man-made barriers might be called *institutional barriers.* They are not legally constituted, as are zoning barriers, nor individually created, as are land speculations. Rather they are unofficial, socially-regulated—and quite effective— mechanisms for discriminating among activities which can pass through into an area. There is, for example, nothing legal to prevent a black family from buying a home in the same neighborhoods as a white family with comparable income. But "somehow" there are no vacancies when blacks search out the area. (Fortunately, these conditions are now changing—although slowly.)

Still other man-made barriers might best be described as *social-psychological barriers.* There is nothing, for example, either legal or institutional, to prevent a white middle-class family from moving into an all-black middle-class area. Yet this seldom occurs. Conversely, black families are wisely cautious about moving into all-white areas.

In summary, the presence of these natural and man-made barriers, some permanent but most temporary, some universal but most discriminating, are major factors in shaping the urban environment. Within the constraints set up by these various barriers, the multitude of social and economic activities, some complementary and some repelling, "compete" for the sites which are available.

Parametric Shifts

If all barriers were permanent; if societal values remained constant; if technological advances were few and far between; then, the shape of the urban environment would soon stabilize and remain reasonably fixed over a considerable time frame. However, none of these conditions holds true.

Most barriers are temporary. Societal values—and resultant tastes and perceived needs—fluctuate rapidly. Technology moves steadily onward offering new possibilities and startling new directions. Thus, the shape of the urban environment, while predictable (because of the presence of complementary and repelling processes subjected to identifiable barriers), is in constant flux.

Those factors which tend to have most significant influence upon altering the shape of the urban environment are referred to here as *parametric shifts*. There are essentially two kinds of parametric shifts: 1) those which alter the decision-rules of individual decision-making units and hence alter the "laws" governing the respective spatial diffusion processes and 2) those which alter the types and arrangements of barriers, and hence alter the possible directions of spread of the affected diffusion processes.

Hence, for example, a decision to build a new mass transit system in a city serves as a parametric shift. Businesses which depend on being accessible to the flows of commuters or shoppers are forced to reassess their present or planned future locations in light of the impact of the system on "people flow." Individual homeowners or renters will reassess their residential locations vis-a-vis the opportunities made possible by the system. These individual assessments and subsequently altered decisions concerning location will collectively produce new "laws" governing the diffusion of these and related activities.

Or, for example, a decision to rezone an area from residential to commercial serves as a parametric shift. Commercial activities which formerly were barred from penetrating into the area are suddenly able to do so. This will affect not only the positions of activities which decide to take advantage of the new zoning, but competitors who do not. Also, the flow of commercial activities into the area causes shifts in the residential patterns of the area as well. To consider another example, the decision by some "bohemians" to move into a rundown area and renovate existing houses will lead to others attempting the same thing nearby. As momentum builds up, the neighborhood may suddenly become "fashionable." As a result, social-psychological barriers which formerly made the area unacceptable for upper and middle income housing are lowered, and the area is "invaded" by such housing types.

Parametric shifts may produce a positive or a negative impact. The effect of a positive parametric shift is to increase the potential profitability (in the economic sense) and/or the potential desirability (in the social sense) of the impacted area. The consequence of such a shift is the maintenance or expansion of existing

11

activities and the possible entry of new activities to the area. Conversely, a negative parametric shift decreases the potential profitability and/or desirability of the impacted area, and leads to the decay and possibly to the death of existing activities.

Of course, what may be a positive parametric shift for one type of activity, might be a neutral or negative shift for some other activities. A decision to construct an elevated freeway through a portion of a city, for example, is beneficial to certain activities along the route and detrimental to others, depending upon a number of additional factors. The riots of the summer of 1968, produced short-range liabilities to both local businessmen and the local community, and resulted in the subsequent "death" of many economic activities. However, some believe that the riots of 1968 were necessary steps in a political and social process still in adolescence. According to this perspective, the riots would be viewed as positive parametric shifts.

Synthesis

Thus, in summary, the urban environment can be interpreted as being shaped by sets of social and economic spatial diffusion processes ("birth" and "death" processes). Processes are complementary (compatible and mutually-advantageous) or repelling (incompatible and perceived as disadvantageous). The spread of these processes is dictated by the degree of their mutual compatibility and by the presence of natural and man-made barriers which impede the spread in given directions of selected processes. Parametric shifts result in changes in individual decisions or in the lowering or alteration of barriers, and consequently redirect the spread of the various processes.

This systemic interpretation of the spatial dynamics underlying the urban environment is consistent with the properties outlined above in the opening chapter. For the purposes of this Paper, this interpretation will serve as the framework or gestalt within which the urban environment is examined through the use of simulation techniques. Following a short introduction to simulation, the general topic of computer simulation will be treated. This will be followed immediately with a computer model illustrating the effects of barriers on the spread of a spatial diffusion process. Gaming simulation models will next be discussed, followed by a presentation of a series of games which focus on different aspects of the urban environment, with particular emphasis on spatial elements.

CHAPTER THREE

WHAT IS SIMULATION?

A simulation, *per se,* is a cross between a portrait and a caricature of reality. It is an attempt to present reality—or more particularly, some facets of reality—in a convincing manner for purposes of explanation, manipulation and analysis. The numbers and varieties of simulation which man has devised for understanding his universe are endless.

For example, every work of literature—both fiction and non-fiction—is a form of simulation. Orwell's *1984,* Huxley's *Brave New World,* and Hesse's *The Bead Game* are in a very real sense attempts by their authors to simulate the direction society could move in if certain prevailing symptoms caught hold and dominated. The American Western, at its best, is an attempt to simulate a part of America's glorious past. Newspaper articles are attempts to simulate some small part of our present world. In what sense are these all simulations? In the sense that they systematically select certain aspects of life to illuminate and manipulate and that they collapse time so that the reader in minutes can experience hours, days, years and centuries.

There are two key ingredients of any simulation:

1) the systematic selection of a small number of features of reality for explanation, manipulation and analysis;

2) the collapsing and/or expanding of the time scale.

A simulation model is a simulation which is governed by some predetermined and consistent rules for handling and manipulating events and information as they are introduced into the simulation. The creator of the simulation model need not be a participant in the simulation as it unfolds. The rules of logic which he has invented and built into the model are sufficient to govern the play of the simulation once it has been activated. Thus, the only work of literature which would be considered a simulation model would be those recent attempts at having computers write books.

There are two quite different types of simulation models of particular interest to urbanists. The first treats society—or that part of society under investigation—as a system of interacting variables which blindly respond to data introduced into the system externally. For example, consider an overly simplified simulation model which does nothing more than check if a parcel of land is vacant or occupied; and if vacant allows it to be occupied, and if occupied signals the potential occupant to try somewhere else. The person operating the simulation feeds in a list of first, second and third choices of several potential home builders for various parcels of land in some predetermined order. The simulation model then assigns each builder to a parcel of land. If a particular builder cannot be assigned a vacant parcel after his three choices are tested in turn, he is placed on a waiting list. The result of this simple simulation is a list of builders and parcel assignments plus a waiting list of those not satisfied. This type of simulation usually requires the aid of electronic data processing to manipulate the various data, and the model is basically no more than an elaborate computer program. Thus, it is generally referred to as *computer simulation.* (Figure 2).

Figure 2

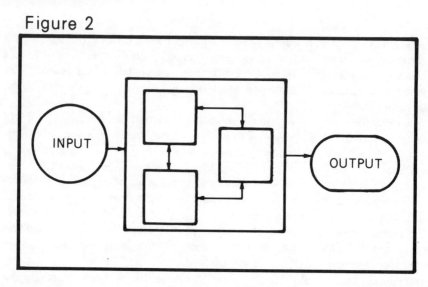

The second type of simulation is one in which the model of some institution or organization is imbedded into the rules of a game, and the play or the game is carried out using strategies and tactics typical of the real world. In it, the critical operations are to a large extent performed by human players attempting to apply their experience and common sense to the best of their ability. The emphasis is on role playing and the possibilities for integrating these respective roles in a way which yields the highest net return to the players. This type of simulation is usually referred to as *gaming simulation.* (Figure 3).

Note the difference between these two forms of simulation. In computer simulation, all moves and strategies are preset and programmed into the model. In gaming simulation, the moves and strategies are invented "on the spot" and limited only by the constraints placed on the game and on the various roles. In computer simulation, there are no live players. What then are some of the relative advantages of each of the two techniques?

1. A computer simulation can perform hundreds of runs (sequences of inputs, moves, and outcomes) in minutes, while a gaming simulation may take hours to produce one run.

2. A computer simulation by virtue of its speed can continually test a situation until a clear pattern of outcomes emerges; a gaming simulation can only be run a few times, and no consistent results may emerge.

14

Figure 3

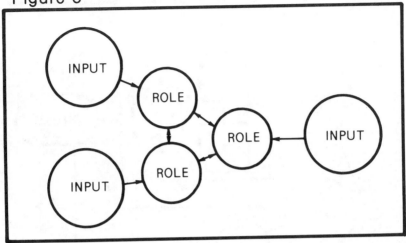

3. In a short time interval, various assumptions and hypotheses can be tested with a computer simulation; whereas only one or a few can be tested with a gaming simulation.

4. The creation of computer simulation requires a clearly stated and well understood "theory" of behavior; the creation of a gaming simulation model requires only a set of behavior characteristics of an institutional framework, and does not require a theory integrating these characteristics into rules of action.

5. In computer simulation, there is little or no interaction with the model as it performs its programmed steps; in gaming simulation, both the creator of the game and the participating players are actively engaged in a learning process during the actual running of the simulation.

6. Computer simulation tests hypotheses and assumptions for validity and uses empirical data to verify the results; gaming simulation studies behavior and role interaction, and its success depends less on its results than on the experiences gained while playing the game.

Thus, these two types of simulation models are quite different both in style (structure) and objectives. Some urban model designers have fruitfully combined the attributes of computer simulation with those of gaming simulation in what might be referred to as man-machine simulation models or, more simply, *computerized gaming simulations*. As the following illustration depicts, these models soon become very complex and cumbersome. (Figure 4).

In the chapters which follow, these two types of simulation models have been treated separately, although a discussion of computerized gaming models is included under gaming simulation. Illustrative examples are included for both techniques. Because of the wide usage of computer and gaming simulation in the

Figure 4

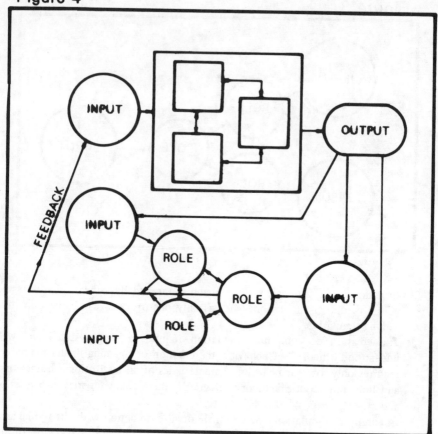

many disparate disciplines and professions concerned with the urban environment, it was necessary to limit the frame of reference in this Paper. Accordingly, the primary focus has been on urban spatial processes (that is, the dynamics through which urban activities distribute themselves throughout the area). However, other complementary areas (such as, for example, the financial plight of the welfare recipient) have been introduced to broaden the perspective of the reader regarding the uses of simulation in studies of the urban environment.

CHAPTER FOUR

COMPUTER SIMULATION

Introduction

In studying the urban environment, computers can often perform useful functions. They can be used to store large amounts of data, which can be retrieved virtually instantaneously. They can perform computations with the data at remarkably rapid speed when compared against human calculation time. They can print out information in most any format desired, including numerical arrays, written text, and graphical presentations. (Figure 5).

The drudgery of performing repetitive calculations by hand is a task people have long sought to escape. The abacus and the desk calculator were designed to ease these burdens. The computer extended these instruments by offering a memory (the storage of data until needed) and a print out capability, as well as a capacity to perform calculations with blinding speed.

Despite their remarkable versatility, computers—at least thus far—must be told what to do. This is called *programming*. The programmer determines which data will be utilized, how it will be stored and manipulated, and finally what will be printed and in which format. These instructions must be translated into a form and vocabulary which the given computer being used is designed to accept. This process is called *coding*.

One problem with using computers for many people is the disproportionate amount of their time which is spent coding as opposed to programming. This is particularly true for the casual user who lacks access to technical support. However,

Figure 5

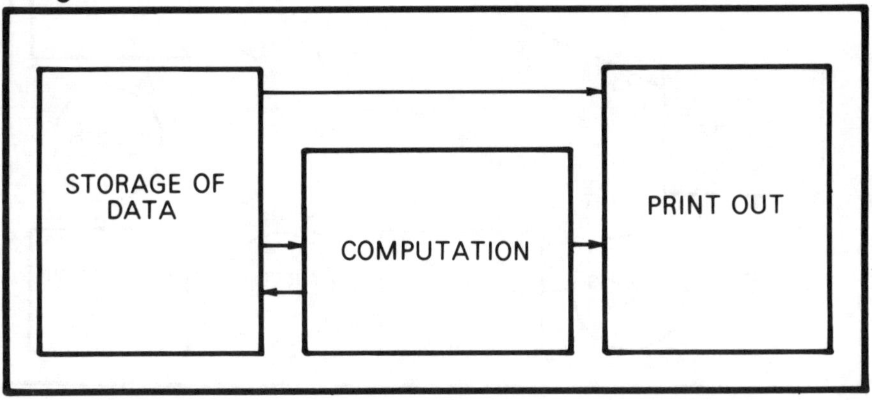

17

there is an ever-increasing supply of prepared computer programs, which can be obtained intact and utilized by the novice programmer. This allows even casual users to quickly reach the stage where they can fruitfully gain insights and/or save considerable time and effort through the utilization of a computer.

Specifically, the role of the computer in simulation work can be categorized for initial discussion into two major groupings: deterministic models and probabilistic (or stochastic) models. A *deterministic model* is one which utilizes no random or chance variables. Each event which will occur within the model is known with 100 percent certainty. Thus, for example, the life cycle *in aggregate* terms is a deterministic model. Animals are born, grow and develop, mate, propagate, age and die. Clearly, a given individual creature may not complete all steps in the cycle. For example, it might be born but die soon thereafter. Or, it might live a long life but for certain reasons never propagate any offsprings (as for example has been known to happen to animals captured and placed in zoos). A *probabilistic model* might therefore be used to gauge the likelihood that any given creature would complete the entire life cycle. At each stage in the process there would exist a certain probability (based upon aggregated and subaggregated past experiences with that species, plus any new factors which might alter past experiences) of successfully completing the next stage. These probabilities, stage by stage, would cumulatively yield an overall probability for various subgroupings of the species in question of successful completion of all stages of the life cycle. (Figure 6).

The reader should note that a deterministic model is in fact a special case of a

Figure 6

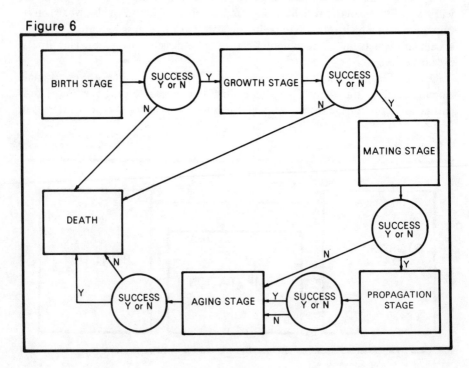

probabilistic model where all probability assignments are either 1.0 or 0.0; that is, events either occur with absolute certainty or don't occur with equal certainty. Thus, while one can talk about deterministic models or about probabilistic models, it is perhaps more appropriate to use the terminology of "deterministic elements" and "probabilistic (or stochastic) elements." Hence, a deterministic model can be discussed as a model containing only deterministic elements. The use of these elements in computer simulation is discussed below.

Sensitivity Analysis

One fruitful area in which computer simulation has been applied is in the testing of the influences of a given factor or set of factors on the overall system under investigation. Thus, for example, if the investigator is interested in demonstrating the effects of one-way versus two-way streets on traffic patterns in a city, he could begin with a completely two-way system and simulate the traffic flowing through it. He would next begin to introduce one-way streets in different locations and note the differences in the traffic flow. In a methodical manner, he could eventually test a multitude of variations—including possibly an entire one-way street system.

He would then be in a better position to posit the effects of one-way streets on traffic flow. Since one is investigating how sensitive the system is to changes in the factor, this type of investigation may be referred to as *sensitivity analysis.*

The above example might be accomplished with purely deterministic elements or with probabilistic elements. For example, a rule might be established for the simulation that an individual wishing to go from point A to point B will *always* travel in as straight a line as possible, regardless of the volume of traffic on the road. This would be a deterministic rule. However, an additional rule might be introduced which states that an individual confronted with a volume of traffic in excess of some critical level may select (say 25 percent of the time) to shift to the second straightest route available (if it is not also saturated with traffic). This would be a probabilistic element, in that certain *individuals* whose identities are *unknown* at the start of the simulation will deviate from the straight line route as a consequence of chance.

Monte Carlo Simulation

A second area in which computer simulations have been applied with regularity is the study of behavior of actors operating within a system. For example, an investigator might be interested in building a model which reproduces the shopping patterns of female office workers during their lunch break. Such a model might be based on sets of probabilities which reflect the options open to these office workers and their posited propensities for shopping. Thus, for illustration, it might be assumed that 75 percent of the females will eat lunch out of their office; that of these "outside eaters," 80 percent will come upon shopping opportunities if they go east and 30 percent will find shopping opportunities if they go west, north or south; that the chances of going in any of these four directions for lunch is even;

19

that 10 percent of all those who come upon an opportunity will make a purchase; and finally that of those who make a purchase, 30 percent will make a second purchase as well. No one will make more than two purchases. To simulate this behavioral model, the following approach could be used:

1. For any individual, determine whether she will eat in or out. To do this, draw a random card from a deck of 100 cards marked "1" through "100" consecutively. If the number drawn is between 1 and 25, assume the individual will eat in. (No purchases. Move on to next individual). If the number is between 26 and 100 assume the individual will eat out. (Continue to step 2.)

2. For any individual eating out, determine the direction she will go. Draw a new random card from the complete deck (having replaced the card drawn above). If the number is between 1 and 25, assume the individual will go east. (Continue to step 3.) If the number drawn is between 26 and 100, assume the female will go non-east (west, north or south—it doesn't matter for this given simulation since these three directions are all governed by identical subsequent probabilities) for lunch. (Continue to step 4, *not* 3.)

3. For all females going east for lunch, draw a new random card from the complete deck. If the number drawn is between 1 and 20 assume no shopping opportunities will be found. (No purchases. Move on to next individual.) If the number is between 21 and 100, assume opportunities are found. (Continue to step 5, *not* 4.)

4. For all females going non-east for lunch, draw a new random card from the complete deck. If the number drawn is between 1 and 70, assume no shopping opportunities will be found. (No purchases. Move on to next individual.) If the number is between 71 and 100, assume opportunities are found. (Continue to step 5.)

5. For those females finding opportunities, draw a new random card from the complete deck. If the number drawn is between 1 and 90, assume no purchases are made. (No purchases. Move on to next individual.) If the number drawn is between 91 and 100, assume at least one purchase is made. (Continue to step 6.)

6. For those females making purchases, draw a new random card from the complete deck. If the number drawn is between 1 and 70, assume that a single purchase is made. (Purchases equal one. Move on to next individual.) If the number drawn is between 71 and 100, assume that two purchases are made. (Purchases equal two. Move on to next individual.)

This oversimplified model of shopping patterns demonstrates how a simulation of this type of behavior might be developed. Because of the "gambling nature" of the model ("pick a number from the deck, if it is between 1 and 80 you lose, if it is between 81 and 100 you win"), such models are often referred to as *Monte Carlo simulations*.

Applications of Computer Simulation

The possible applications of computer simulation in the study of the urban environment are virtually endless. Any phenomenon which can be explained may potentially be simulated. To the extent to which the investigator or teacher is interested in dealing with increasingly complex systems or subsystems, the ability to profit from thoughtful use of computer simulation models will increase proportionately or perhaps more exponentially.

In many cases, the discipline and skills developed in constructing the model and the sets of instructions needed to make it operational, and in obtaining the data and probability sets to plug into the model, will far outweigh the outputs (printouts) obtained in terms of their impact on the individual. But this is good. Understanding how a system works is as valid an undertaking as predicting what it will produce. In fact, the latter result invariably defines itself upon successful completion of the former task.

In designing or working with computers in general, and computer simulations specifically, one must always be on the look-out for what is often referred to as "G.I.G.O." or "garbage in, garbage out." Getting a computer to run (to accept data and print results) is one thing, getting it to produce relevant and correct results is quite another thing. In attempts to get their models operating, many designers have made the mistake of oversimplifying steps to the degree that the results obtained are highly suspect. Others have built models which are overelaborate, given the availability of usable data. Hence, a proper balance must be achieved between sophistication (to reflect the nuances and richness of interrelationships) and comparability of data quality and model quality.

In the chapter which follows, a simple but interesting model of spatial diffusion is presented in some detail. It was designed by the author to explore and illustrate some of the elements of spatial dynamics discussed in Chapter Two.

CHAPTER FIVE

A COMPUTER MODEL OF SPATIAL GROWTH

Introduction

In attempting to understand a complex process, it is often helpful to develop a less complex analogue for use in preliminary investigations. Wind tunnel experimentation, for example, has yielded valuable insights to aircraft designers investigating new concepts in aerodynamics. In this chapter, an analogue of urban spatial processes is presented which was utilized by the author in his early conceptualization of the dynamics of urban spatial processes. The analogue is an extension of a spatial diffusion model originally developed by Torsten Hägerstrand in his study of migration in Sweden. Hägerstrand's work is first presented, followed by a discussion and illustration of the adaptations made. An interpretation of the results generated is then presented.

Spatial Diffusion

The initial impetus for the work on spatial diffusion can be linked to a Swedish cultural anthropologist named Sigfrid Svensson. However, the major credit for bringing spatial diffusion models to prominence is rightly given to the Swedish geographer, Torsten Hägerstrand. Hägerstrand addressed himself to the problem of studying how a new cultural phenomenon spreads over space once it has been introduced, and he chose simulation as his technique for tackling this problem.

Hägerstrand inductively generalized that the diffusion of any new cultural phenomenon recently introduced into an area can be described as follows:

    a) in the first stage, there is a local concentration of initial acceptances of the innovation;

    b) in the second stage, there is a radial dissemination outward from the initial agglomeration, accompanied by the rise of secondary agglomerations, and the continual condensation of the original agglomerations;

    c) in the final stage, saturation sets in and the growth ceases.

In order to simulate such a growth process, it is necessary to specify the rate at which acceptances occur and the probability distribution of these acceptances over space. Thus, in order to simulate the spread of color television ownerships, one would need to know the number of new households which would buy such a television each day (or week or month) and the probability that these households would be located in selected communities. Intuitively, one would expect that the more contact one household has with those households which have purchased color sets, the more likely the former household would be to purchase its own set (presuming the sets seen are working well). In most cases, in fact, the probability distributions describing the likelihood of acceptance of an innovation reflect that proximity to persons who have accepted the innovation increases the chance of further acceptance by others.

Applications of this concept of spatial diffusion have been made in a number of diverse subject areas, including the spread of information, social and political behavior, educational programs, disease and economic activities. Of particular interest to the study of urban spatial processes is the work done on the spread of population resulting from urban growth and inter-urban and intra-urban migration. The following work by Hägerstrand was one of the pioneering efforts in this area, and serves as the prototype for much of the work which has consequently been undertaken in the field of simulation of population dispersion. (It first appeared in English in the Lund Studies in Geography, Series B, Human Geography, No. 13, 1957, pages 27–158.)

Hägerstrand's Migration Model

While studying the spatial distribution of outmigrants from a Swedish parish, Torsten Hägerstrand noted that neither the "laws" of inverse distance (the further away a location is, the less likely it is to attract a migrant) nor intervening opportunities (the immediate opportunities for new locations are more likely to cease than subsequent ones) were adequate to explain what he observed. The Swedish migrants were distinctly clustered in certain areas and absent in what would have seemed to be "attractive" locations, leading Hägerstrand to conclude that this phenomenon was at least in part due to a cumulative process reminiscent of cultural diffusion; i.e., one emigrant in selecting a destination was dependent on earlier emigrants. Hägerstrand noted that other studies conducted around this time (mid-1950's) by Kant of Budapest, Pinkney of Paris, and Larrson of the Swedish west coast resulted in similar conclusions. Thus, migration could not be regarded simply as cohorts of people being shifted from place to place according to some predetermined rules, but should be viewed at least in part as a dynamic chain of connected events.

What is suggested then is that there are at least two types of migrants: active migrants, who independently choose a suitable destination guaranteeing future prosperity (as measured according to their personal value structures), and passive migrants, who follow after persons who are perceived to have made "fortunate" moves. In the course of an individual's life several moves are made, and among these are likely to be both passive and active ones—with the latter possibly generating passive moves by others.

Hägerstrand attempted to reproduce the migration history of a rural Swedish area with an experimental model incorporating both active and passive moves. Rules for the spread of a limited number of migrants within a limited range of migration were defined as follows:

1. Migration occurs over a featureless plain subdivided into cells ("parishes") spaced equidistant over the entire plain. The cells are designated (x,y). The

24

plain is operationally unbounded; i.e., a migrant always has the possibility of moving farther out from the origin (although the rules are such that the range of migration is small even for a reasonably large number of iterations). The cells have unlimited capacity to absorb migrants; i.e., there is no ceiling to the number of migrants occupying a given cell at any time.

2. All migrations start from the origin (0,0). In each iteration 50 individuals undertake their first migration. (Thus, after the first iteration there are 50 migrants; after the second iteration there are 100 migrants; after the third iteration there are 150 migrants, etc.).

3. The number of moves (including the first migration) an individual has in his lifetime is determined according to the following probability table (an adjusted version of probabilities generated by Wendell in 1953):

P(1) = .25	P(5) = .09	P(9) = .02
P(2) = .22	P(6) = .05	P(10) = .01
P(3) = .16	P(7) = .04	P(11) = .01
P(4) = .12	P(8) = .03	

4. The interval (in number of iterations) between two moves by the same individual is determined according to the following probability table (also attributable to Wendell with modifications):

P(0) = .200	P(10) = .015	P(20) = .003
P(1) = .200	P(11) = .015	P(21) = .003
P(2) = .150	P(12) = .010	P(22) = .002
P(3) = .100	P(13) = .010	P(23) = .002
P(4) = .080	P(14) = .008	P(24) = .002
P(5) = .060	P(15) = .008	P(25) = .002
P(6) = .040	P(16) = .006	
P(7) = .030	P(17) = .006	
P(8) = .020	P(18) = .004	
P(9) = .020	P(19) = .004	

(Note: P(0) = .200 implies that 20% of the time an individual who has just migrated and has additional moves left in his lifetime will move again in the same iteration).

5. There are two types of moves, active migrations and passive migrations.

6. An active migration by an individual is independent of past moves of other migrants. The individual can choose to move to one of the eight adjacent cells only, and has an equal chance of moving to any. Thus, the following probabilities hold for an active move from cell (x,y):

$$P(\text{destination} = (x-1, y+1)) = .125$$
$$P(\text{destination} = (x, y+1)) = .125$$
$$P(\text{destination} = (x+1, y)) = .125$$
$$P(\text{destination} = (x+1, y-1)) = .125$$
$$P(\text{destination} = (x, y-1)) = .125$$
$$P(\text{destination} = (x-1, y-1)) = .125$$
$$P(\text{destination} = (x-1, y)) = .125$$
$$P(\text{destination} = (x+1, y+1)) = .125$$

25

7. A passive migrant chooses a new location dependent upon his "acquaintances"; or operationally expressed, a passive migrant has equal probability of being attracted to any past migrant (including those who have returned to the origin). Note that until some migrant has moved actively, passive migrants must remain at the origin.

8. The probability that a first migration from (0,0) is active is .4 and passive .6.

9. Second and subsequent migrants are always active.

As should now be clear to the reader, the model described above is a Monte Carlo simulation. It lends itself readily to computerization. A typical run on a computer of this model would result in the amoebic-like spread effect discussed above in Chapter Two. Such a run is illustrated on the next page. (Figure 7)

Experimentation with the Hägerstrand Migration Model

The amoeba-like pattern depicted could be interpreted as simulating unchecked urban sprawl in which land development opportunities are available in all directions out from the urban core and accessibility is ubiquitous. The rate of population growth could be modified by increasing or decreasing the number of new migrants in each iteration. The speed with which peripheral development occurs could be changed by modifying the probability schedule governing the direction of active moves. If, for example, the simulation of more rapid outward sprawl were desired, the probabilities assigned to outward moves could be increased and the probabilities assigned to inward moves comparably decreased.

Even more interesting from the point-of-view of studying urban spatial dynamics, various shaped barriers could be placed at different locations on the migration field vis-a-vis the origin, and the consequent alterations in the pattern of sprawl noted. If these barriers were designed so as to simulate different real-world natural and manmade barriers (for example, mountain ranges, rivers, zoned land, freeways), the effects of these on urban spatial development could be studied and compared.

To illustrate this, a series of variations of the Hägerstrand migration model were simulated utilizing different barrier configurations. Both permanent and temporary barriers were examined. A *permanent barrier* is one which remains fixed throughout the entire simulation. A *temporary barrier* is one which can be altered or eliminated during the simulation if certain predefined conditions are met. In order to accelerate the simulated growth process so that temporary irregularities would vanish more readily and consequently the actual growth patterns could more quickly be discerned, the number of new migrants introduced each iteration was increased from 50 to 100.

1. *Reflecting Barrier:* Consider a case like Chicago or Tel Aviv, where growth is restricted to a half-plain because of a water boundary. In order to simulate the expansion pattern from such a city, it is necessary to introduce a reflecting barrier into the model; i.e., to turn back any simulated moves going into the restricted (water) area. This is quite easily accomplished within the framework of the model by "inquiring" if a migrant has moved into a

Figure 7

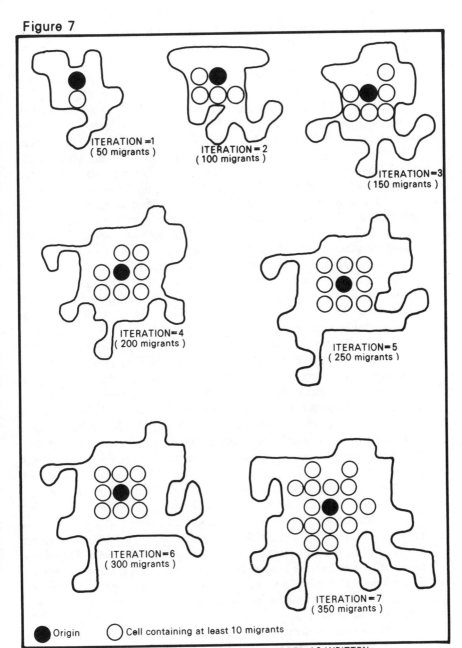

ITERATION = 1
(50 migrants)

ITERATION = 2
(100 migrants)

ITERATION = 3
(150 migrants)

ITERATION = 4
(200 migrants)

ITERATION = 5
(250 migrants)

ITERATION = 6
(300 migrants)

ITERATION = 7
(350 migrants)

● Origin   ○ Cell containing at least 10 migrants

TYPICAL RUN OF HAGERSTRAND MODEL AS WRITTEN

restricted cell, and if so, would send him back to the cell he was in before the move and would have him migrate again. The results for selected iterations of a typical run of this type are illustrated on the following pages (Figures 8 and 9). Clearly other boundaries such as mountains, gorges, or national borders could be treated similarly.

2. *Axes Movement:* It is a commonly observed feature of urban growth that population first spreads out along major transportation arteries (street car lines, highways, etc.) and at a later date the intervening areas fill in. This can be handled easily within the confines of the model by simply adjusting the probabilities governing active moves (rule 6) to reflect the greater likelihood of movement in certain specified directions. To illustrate this, the probabilities associated with an active move were modified as follows: an active migrant had 20% chance of moving horizontally or vertically (both in the positive and negative sense), but only 5% chance of moving diagonally. Results for selected iterations are illustrated below (Figures 10 and 11). These probabilities seemed just sufficient to create a circular growth pattern and insure that the cells along the two axes developed at a pace necessary to keep slightly ahead of non-axes growth. Clearly, different probability assignments for the active moves could result in a wide assortment of patterns, including linear growth (if movement was encouraged along only one axis) or an X-shaped configuration (if diagonal movement was favored and probabilities were assigned of say 24% for a diagonal move and 1% for an axis move.)

3. *Permanent Small Barriers:* Occasionally a city is located alongside a lake or some other permanent small barrier, and growth of the city is greatly influenced by its presence (example: Lucerne). This case can be treated in the same way as the reflecting barrier discussed above, with the single difference that the barrier here is finite in length and it is possible for migrants to work their way around it. Two situations were considered: a) an origin with a small (1 x 3) vertically-oriented barrier alongside it and b) an origin with a small (3 x 1) horizontally oriented barrier alongside it. Results of the two cases for selected iterations are illustrated on the following pages (Figures 12 through 15). As these figures show, although the vertical barrier had a greater ability to keep the majority of migrants from spreading around it, sufficient migrants did so, and the overall extent of growth was surprisingly similar for the two cases. Of course, had the barriers been longer the influence of these barriers would have been more marked. Furthermore, if the spatial relationship between the origin and the barriers was changed, the resultant spatial patterns would have been different.

For most narrow barriers, it may be possible to provide access across these (via bridges, tunnels, ferry services, etc.). The model can be altered to handle this contingency in much the same way as is described next for temporary barriers.

4. *Temporary Small Barriers:* Not all barriers are natural or permanent. Certain areas of an urban or rural region are restricted to non-residential uses

28

Figure 8

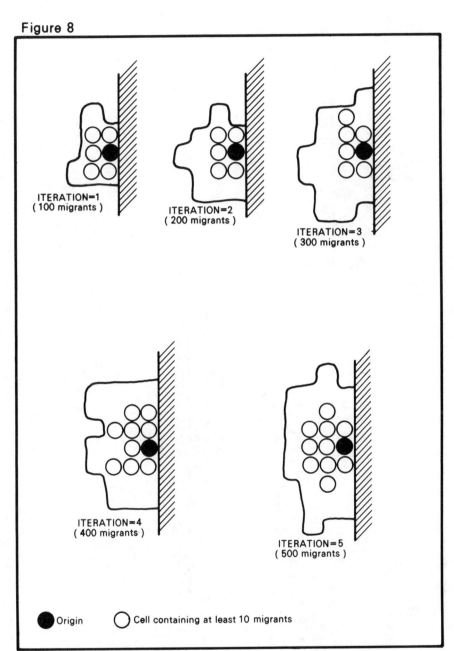

ITERATION=1
(100 migrants)

ITERATION=2
(200 migrants)

ITERATION=3
(300 migrants)

ITERATION=4
(400 migrants)

ITERATION=5
(500 migrants)

● Origin   ○ Cell containing at least 10 migrants

TYPICAL RUN OF HAGERSTRAND MODEL WITH REFLECTING BARRIER

Figure 9

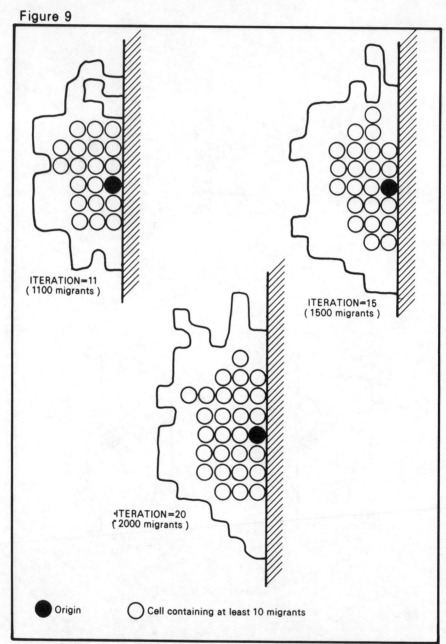

ITERATION=11
(1100 migrants)

ITERATION=15
(1500 migrants)

ITERATION=20
(2000 migrants)

● Origin   ○ Cell containing at least 10 migrants

TYPICAL RUN OF HAGERSTRAND MODEL WITH REFLECTING BARRIER (continued)

Figure 10

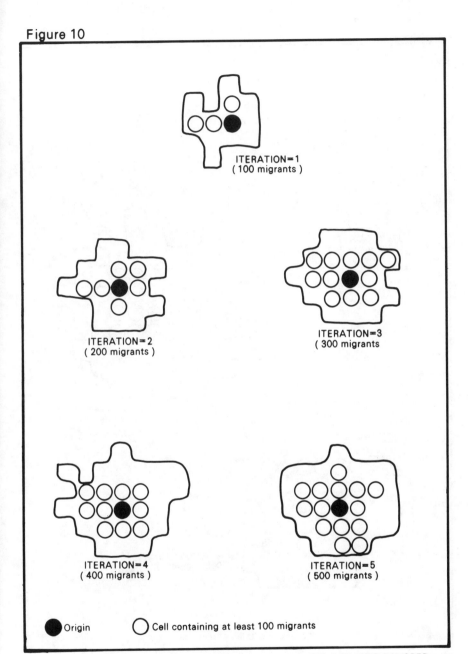

ITERATION=1
(100 migrants)

ITERATION=2
(200 migrants)

ITERATION=3
(300 migrants

ITERATION=4
(400 migrants)

ITERATION=5
(500 migrants)

● Origin   ○ Cell containing at least 100 migrants

TYPICAL RUN OF HAGERSTRAND MODEL WITH N-S AND E-W AXES FAVORED

Figure 11

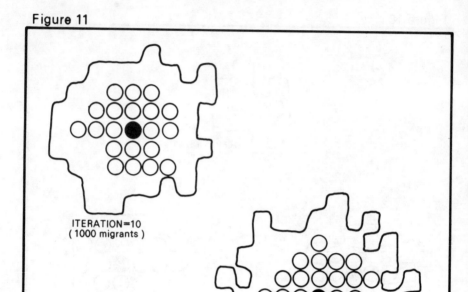

ITERATION=10
(1000 migrants)

ITERATION=15
(1500 migrants)

ITERATION=20
(2000 migrants)

● Origin   ○ Cell containing at least 10 mh migrants

TYPICAL RUN OF HAGERSTRAND MODEL WITH N-S AND E-W AXES FAVORED (continued)

Figure 12

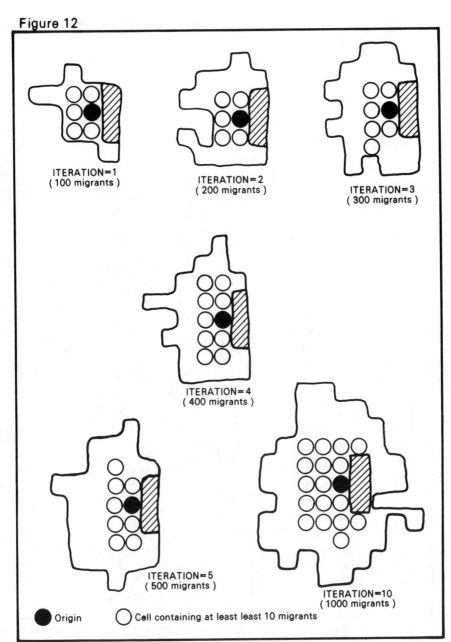

ITERATION=1
(100 migrants)

ITERATION=2
(200 migrants)

ITERATION=3
(300 migrants)

ITERATION=4
(400 migrants)

ITERATION=5
(500 migrants)

ITERATION=10
(1000 migrants)

● Origin   ○ Cell containing at least least 10 migrants

TYPICAL RUN OF HAGERSTRAND MODEL WITH PERMANENT VERTICAL BARRIER

33

Figure 13

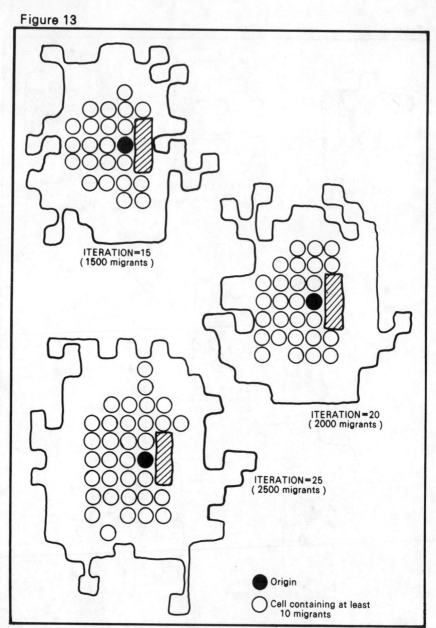

ITERATION=15
(1500 migrants)

ITERATION=20
(2000 migrants)

ITERATION=25
(2500 migrants)

● Origin

○ Cell containing at least
   10 migrants

TYPICAL RUN OF HAGERSTRAND MODEL WITH PERMANENT VERTICAL BARRIER(continued)

Figure 14

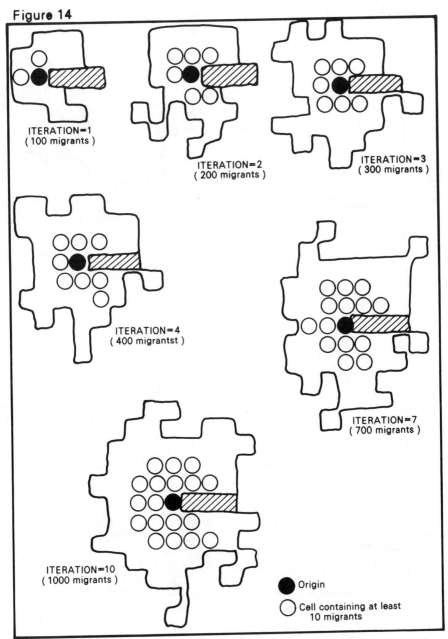

ITERATION=1
(100 migrants)

ITERATION=2
(200 migrants)

ITERATION=3
(300 migrants)

ITERATION=4
(400 migrantst)

ITERATION=7
(700 migrants)

ITERATION=10
(1000 migrants)

● Origin

○ Cell containing at least
10 migrants

TYPICAL RUN OF HAGERSTRAND MODEL WITH PERMANENT HORIZONTAL BARRIER

35

Figure 15

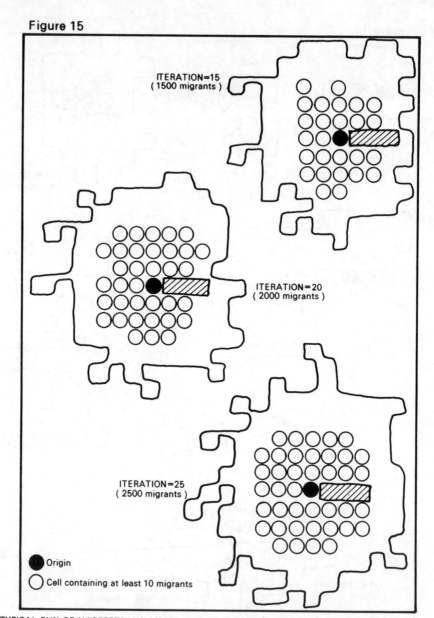

ITERATION=15
(1500 migrants)

ITERATION=20
(2000 migrants)

ITERATION=25
(2500 migrants)

● Origin

○ Cell containing at least 10 migrants

TYPICAL RUN OF HAGERSTRAND MODEL WITH PERMANENT HORIZONTAL BARRIER (continued)

(examples: parks, industrial zones, college campuses, farmland) or are unsuited for residential development unless modified (example: marshlands). Due to different combinations of social, economic and political factors, such temporary barriers can possibly be removed (i.e., the land use changed) and made attractive for immigration. The temporary barrier situation can be handled within the model framework as follows: a) determine the amount of "pressure" needed to convert the non-residential land to residential (operationally, determine the critical number of "hits" on the barrier sufficient to cause its removal, where a "hit" means that an active migrant has moved to a cell within the barrier and has been sent back to move again); b) proceed as in the case of the small permanent barrier, only keeping count of the number of hits; c) if the critical number of hits is reached, eliminate the barrier and proceed as in the original Hägerstrand model without barriers.

Two cases were considered, namely the same configurations as were used above for the permanent small barriers, only this time allowing the vertical or horizontal barrier to break down after 100 hits. Results for selected iterations appear in Figures 16 through 19. As is noted, while the vertical barrier is a more effective decelerator of migration flows in the direction of the barrier from the origin, it is also more prone to being hit (since it presents more cells to the population center).

5. *Outside Attraction Fields:* While the Hägerstrand model was intended to illustrate how migration spreads from a single origin over a limited plain, there are many multi-centered situations of interest to geographers and planners which can fit into the model's format. Consider, for example, the case of two neighboring sites in the region of origin which have some attraction for migrants. Assume that some of the new migrants, rather than settle around the origin, are attracted to one of the two other centers. One might then examine how many iterations are required for the three areas to grow together into a single area.

The above case was programmed as follows: Let the origin be at $(0,0)$. Allow the 100 new migrants in each iteration to have 80% chance of starting from the origin, 6% chance of initially being attracted to $(7,5)$ and 14% chance of initially being attracted to $(-8,6)$. As in the previous cases, all moves after the first are active. Reflecting barriers were placed at $x = -10$ and $x = 11$ and at $y = 8$ to keep all migrants within a fixed region. Typical results of this program for selected iterations appear in figures on following pages (Figures 20 through 22).

Application

There are an endless number of variations which could be handled with a model of this type. By altering the number, position, sizes and orientation of the various barriers, by including both permanent and temporary barriers and by phasing the introduction of these barriers at the various positions; any pattern of growth can be simulated. Superimposing diffusion processes from different origins and with

37

Figure 16

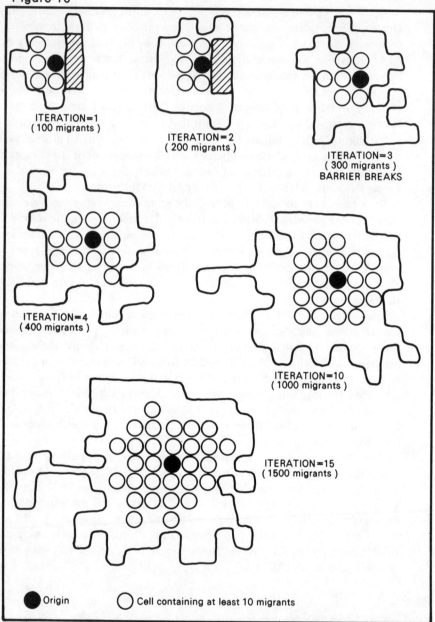

ITERATION=1
(100 migrants)

ITERATION=2
(200 migrants)

ITERATION=3
(300 migrants)
BARRIER BREAKS

ITERATION=4
(400 migrants)

ITERATION=10
(1000 migrants)

ITERATION=15
(1500 migrants)

● Origin   ○ Cell containing at least 10 migrants

TYPICAL RUN OF HAGERSTRAND MODEL WITH TEMPORARY VERTICAL BARRIER

38

Figure 17

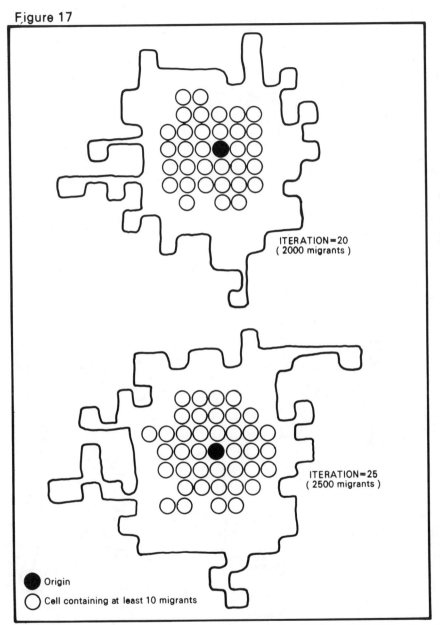

ITERATION=20
(2000 migrants)

ITERATION=25
(2500 migrants)

● Origin
○ Cell containing at least 10 migrants

TYPICAL RUN OF HAGERSTRAND MODEL WITH TEMPORARY VERTICAL BARRIER (continued)

Figure 18

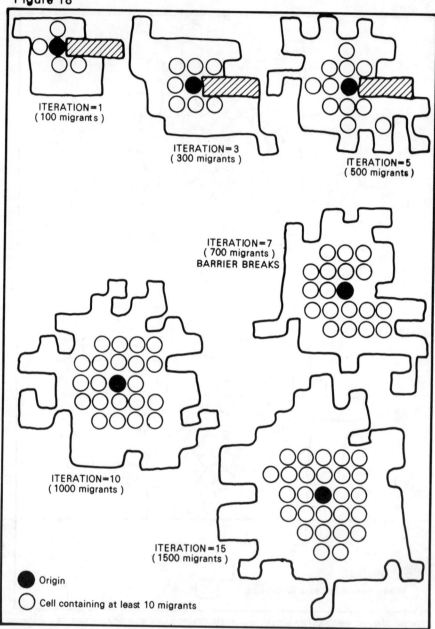

ITERATION=1
(100 migrants)

ITERATION=3
(300 migrants)

ITERATION=5
(500 migrants)

ITERATION=7
(700 migrants)
BARRIER BREAKS

ITERATION=10
(1000 migrants)

ITERATION=15
(1500 migrants)

● Origin

○ Cell containing at least 10 migrants

TYPICAL RUN OF HAGERSTRAND MODEL WITH TEMPORARY HORIZONTAL BARRIER

40

Figure 19

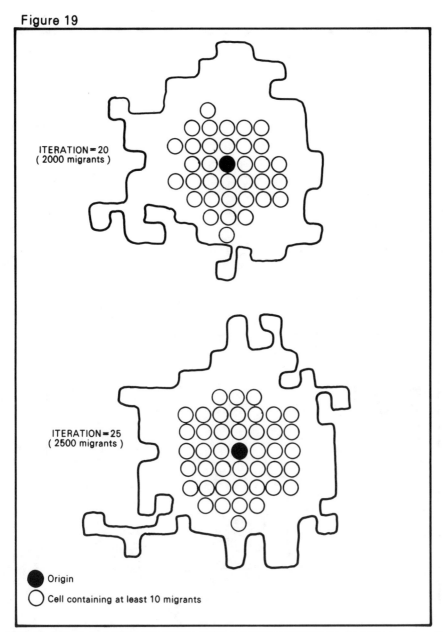

ITERATION = 20
(2000 migrants)

ITERATION = 25
(2500 migrants)

● Origin
○ Cell containing at least 10 migrants

TYPICAL RUN OF HAGERSTRAND MODEL WITH TEMPORY HORIZONTAL BARRIER (continued)

41

Figure 20

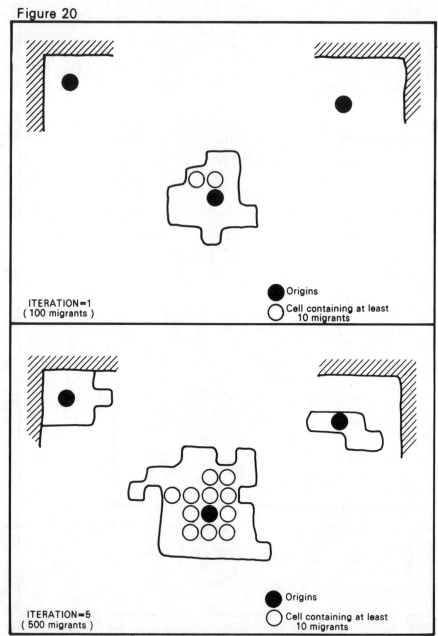

ITERATION=1
(100 migrants)

● Origins

○ Cell containing at least
10 migrants

ITERATION=5
(500 migrants)

● Origins

○ Cell containing at least
10 migrants

TYPICAL RUN OF HAGERSTRAND MODEL WITH TWO OUTSIDE ATTRACTION FIELDS

42

Figure 21

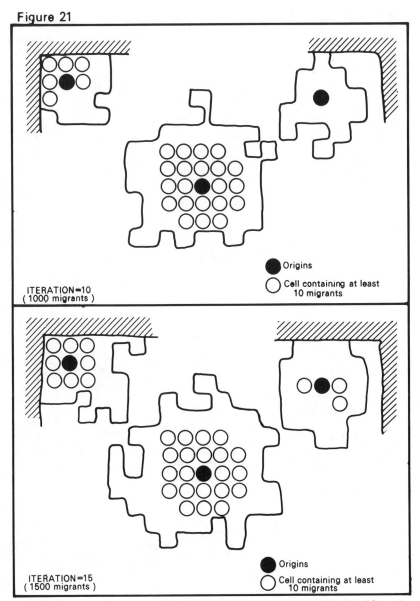

ITERATION=10
(1000 migrants)

● Origins

○ Cell containing at least
10 migrants

ITERATION=15
(1500 migrants)

● Origins

○ Cell containing at least
10 migrants

TYPICAL RUN OF HAGERSTRAND MODEL WITH TWO OUTSIDE ATTRACTION FIELDS (continued)

43

Figure 22

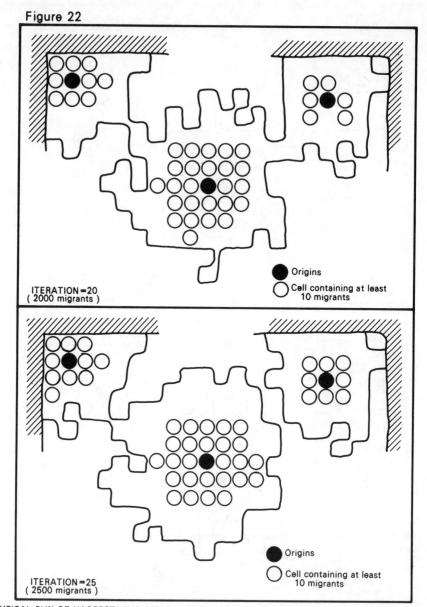

ITERATION = 20
(2000 migrants)

Origins

Cell containing at least
10 migrants

ITERATION = 25
(2500 migrants)

Origins

Cell containing at least
10 migrants

TYPICAL RUN OF HAGERSTRAND MODEL WITH TWO OUTSIDE ATTRACTION FIELDS (continued)

differing rates of growth, complex patterns of spatial diffusion can be generated. Rules can be imposed regarding the manner in which these different processes may interact. The results will be complex representations depicting any spatial form desired. Thus, any urban spatial process can be simulated with a model of this general type.

Consider, for example, the case of the nine county San Francisco Bay Region. As illustrated in the diagram below, the region is rich in natural barriers which contain and channel possible urban growth (Figure 23). The irregularly shaped Bay (actually three bays and a strait) provides a formidable barrier to urban expansion. Surrounding mountains and hills further impede expansion. Yet, what only a half century ago was basically a three-center urban system (San Francisco, Oakland, and San Jose), has become a virtually continuous spread of population across the valleys and bay front. Six bridges span the bay to allow circulation throughout the Region, and thus have effectively served as "barrier breakers." A tunnel cuts through the Berkeley Hills—another "barrier breaker." Land along the bay front is filled to provide development possibilities—yet another "barrier breaker."

Thus the historical spread of the population within the Region is ideally suited for a study utilizing a computer simulation model of the type presented above. To perform such a simulation, the following efforts would be required:

As a first step in the simulation, it would be necessary to perform a topological transformation of the Region to make the study area more amenable to analysis. This would require a two-step procedure: 1) a determination of the basic topographical components of the area and 2) a geometrical simplification of these into rectangular forms such as was done in Figure 23. The "Region" would then need to be subdivided into "uninhabitable areas" (mountains and water) forming impermeable barriers (called "reflecting barriers" in the last section), temporary barriers (the salt flats in the south) and habitable areas. Each subdivision would be further divided into cells.

The following rules might then be set:

1. All habitable cells could be given capacities ranging from say 20 to 100 units, where each unit represents 1000 people; i.e., a maximum of 100,000 people allowed to reside in any cell at any given time. All other cells would have 0 capacity; i.e., they are uninhabitable.

2. The actual urban population in the Region in 1900 (504,000) could be taken as the initial distribution and assigned to appropriate cells (corresponding to actual locations in 1900) as 504 population units.

3. The number of moves a population unit has in its lifetime (*not* including its original placement) could be determined according to the same probability table as was used in the original Hägerstrand model (or adapted on the basis of other available data).

4. The interval between two moves by the same population unit (and between its initial placement and first move) could be determined exactly as in the original model (or adapted on the basis of other available data).

5. 500 new population units could be introduced into the Region each iteration

45

Figure 23

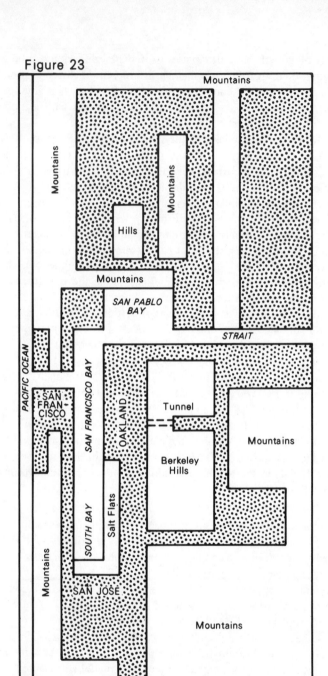

SAN FRANCISCO BAY REGION

Habitable areas

46

by means of a gravity model independent of distance; i.e., each new population unit would have an equal chance of being attracted to the location of any population unit (original or other) which had previously been introduced into the simulation. (The growth simulated corresponds to the fact that the Bay Region did in fact grow by roughly 500,000 per decade during the 20th century).

6. All population units with a move in a current iteration might have say an 80% chance of migrating actively and 20% of migrating passively.

7. An active migration could be defined as in the original model. If the new location is filled to capacity, the population unit would have to return to its original location and attempt another active move. If after 5 moves it can not "find" an unsaturated cell, its move would be forfeited.

8. A passive migration could also be defined as in the original model. If the cell to which the population unit is attracted is filled to capacity, the unit might be allowed to move actively from this cell as part of the same move sequence. If after 5 moves it could not "find" an unsaturated cell, it would return to its original location and its move would be forfeited.

9. Certain barriers would be considered "breakable"; i.e., after a certain number of hits, a population unit would be permitted to "leap over" the barrier and locate on the other side. The rules governing each type of "barrier breaker" could be as follows:

   a. Water barrier breakers might be ferry service after say 25 hits and bridges after say 100 hits. Migrants in the five cells nearest the barrier on either side would be affected. With the bridge, all migrants could leap over the water and have equal chance of being located in one of the five opposite cells. With the ferry service, only one-third of the active migrants (as determined by chance) might be permitted the leap to the other side, while the other two-thirds would repeat the active sequence from its start.

   b. Marginal land barrier breakers could also be introduced in the form of salt flats converted to residential land after say 40 hits; i.e., they were temporary barriers in the sense discussed in the previous section of the paper.

   c. A mountain barrier breaker might also be a tunnel dug after say 50 hits. The five cells on the west side of the barrier nearest the tunnel would be affected. After 50 hits, active migrants from these cells hitting the mountain barrier might be moved with equal chance to one of the three cells immediately beyond the tunnel. Reverse migration through the tunnel would also be possible, but discouraged by allowing only say a 10% chance of moving back through it.

Obviously, the model as presented above is quite crude and several important factors are missing. For example, areas within the region with economic opportunities might well be made more "attractive" to population units than the other cells.

In addition, other factors such as the 1909 earthquake, the depression of the 1930's, the impact of the two World Wars and the Vietnam war would need to be built into any actual simulation (Note: the Bay Area has served as one of the principal supply points for military operations in Vietnam). Yet these adaptations could be made within the framework of the model as presented.*

* The author previously attempted to develop such a simulation model of the Bay Area. Initial results were promising, but competing demands on his time prevented refining the results. Unfortunately, the materials generated are too crude for presentation here.

CHAPTER SIX

GAMING SIMULATION

What is a gaming simulation? Simply stated, it is a role playing exercise which focuses on a given setting and a related set of problems or issues. Participants (players) are assigned roles representing conflicting points of view or objectives. Most often, the goal for each player is to obtain control of—or a large share of—the limited resources (money, land, power, success, etc.) which are available. The overriding purpose for the simulation as a whole is to depict vividly the behavior patterns and related coping strategies implied by the various roles, individually and collectively.

To grasp better the range of gaming simulations, to identify the elements they have in common and also the ways in which they differ, a survey of gaming simulation variations is presented below. This is followed by a section dealing with the design of such games.

War Gaming

In our classes in ancient and modern history we have been taught to admire and/or appreciate the military cunning of the likes of Alexander the Great, Julius Caesar, Napoleon, Generals Lee, Rommel, MacArthur and Dayan—especially their abilities to outguess and outwit their enemies. It is not surprising, therefore, to find today's military strategists fascinated by the prospects of matching wits against hypothetical enemies in complex war games. Besides the psychological rewards of winning the pseudo-war, the military has found war games to be an excellent means for testing out communications and logistics networks, for evaluating alternative strategies, for "ironong out" certain tactical shortcomings, and for testing new equipment and theories.

War gaming can be classified into two broad classes: 1) the "live" game with actual troops deployed in mock battle and 2) the board game, where symbols are used to represent men and equipment. The variety within these two classes is endless, and only a "flavor" of the two can be presented here.

1. *Live War Games*

The live war game usually pits one group of soldiers against another, arming one with the weapons and strategies of the "good guys" and the other with those of their enemy. Each side is given a mission, which may or may not involve interaction with or even knowledge of the other side, and the situation is set so these sides will quickly encounter one another. Reactions to these encounters are gauged, and conclusions drawn.

The key to the success of the live war game from the standpoint of the participants is the extent to which it resembles reality and helps them master their various military assignments. An underlying assumption is that if an individual goes through a gaming experience, he is less likely to commit the same mistakes again in actual combat and will have, on the other hand, collected a series of successful responses and reflexes which may prove useful—if not critical—in battle. *Thus, it is essential that the war game teach the proper lessons.* It is conditioning soldiers to respond in times of stress, and improper conditioning can have disastrous consequences—ranging from individual panic to unnecessary loss of many lives.

From the standpoint of the military planner, a successful war game is one sufficiently controlled so that critical events can be linked to chains of causal factors (rather than being the result of some haphazard side effects) and are reproducible so they can be analyzed after the game is completed. Elaborate data collection equipment becomes mandatory so that the analyst can have his "eyes" on the entire gaming battle area throughout the exercise while at the same time being as inconspicuous as possible. Among the data collection tools utilized are gun cameras mounted to key weapons to record fields of fire; electronic timing devices to record who saw whom first, etc.; field observers with tape recorders, walkie-talkies, and pencil and pad; aerial photography depicting troop deployment at predetermined time intervals; diaries kept by selected participants; and the all-important debriefings to reconstruct events.

Needless to say, "the best laid schemes of mice and men gang aft a-gley . . ." The "live" war game seldom—if ever— goes off exactly as scheduled. Equipment—both tactical and analytical—malfunctions, communications break down, reconstructed events prove to be clearly contradictory or impossible, causal chains of events have broken links, the natural and human environment plays havoc with analytic calm.

Despite this, the live war game can be of extreme value to troops, strategists, and military analysts. The translation of tactics and theories from classified work papers and reports to human actions and reactions in "living color" has proven to be extremely thought-provoking and enlightening. The critics who argue that no war game can ever pretend to recreate the stress and strain of real warfare are not without sound foundations. Yet, *gaming makes no pretense at reproducing reality—nor should it. Its value is in dramatizing human interaction to understand better the subtleties and "irrationalities" imbedded in them. No decisions should be made on the basis of gaming simulations alone. However, the insights gained from a gaming experience often yield analytical fruits which alternative forms of analysis do not lend themselves to producing.*

2. *Military Board Games*

The board games used in military analyses can be thought of as elaborate expansions of the game of chess, in which the competing strategists have only partial knowledge of their opponents' strength and positions. The classic war gaming construct consists of three rooms, commonly referred to (in the United States, at least) as the blue room, the control room, and the red room. 1) In the control room is a scale model of the battle area, with the equipment and personnel of the opposing forces plotted. Umpires set the scenario, solicit and follow the moves of the two sides, pass judgments where appropriate (who killed whom, for example), and terminate the encounter. They then act as moderators for post-game recapitulation and evaluation. 2) In the blue room sits a similar model of the battle area, although it may be distorted or incomplete depending on the knowledge of the blue forces. The blue equipment and personnel are plotted on the model, as are a partial set of red equipment and personnel (which may or may not be accurate or up-to-date). The blue strategists are called upon to make moves to set off a series of encounters with the red forces, or to respond to actions by the red team. They are given additional intelligence information as the game proceeds, as well as data regarding red and blue casualties. 3) The red room is identical to the blue room, except that data and distortion of reality reflect red intelligence information and knowledge.

The board game has proven to be a highly flexible means of examining interaction between opposing military strategy teams in a controlled situation. The use of computers to process moves and compile results has also allowed the playing time of the game to be accelerated so that many variations can be tested in a relatively short period of time. Participants in the simulation—players and umpires—become almost fanatic in their support of the technique. However, its use has received mixed reaction from the Pentagon.

The criticism of the board game is similar to that of the live war game. Just how realistic is the game, and are the lessons learned really relevant when the "chips are down"? Again, a response to this criticism is that gaming is one of several ways of studying military problems—each of which has biases and shortcomings. It is through the triangulation of various techniques that knowledge will be expanded— and the board game despite its weaknesses explores areas where alternative analytic techniques are undeveloped and fragmental at best. Coupled with other forms of analysis, the contribution of gaming to military planning can sometimes prove to be highly valuable.

Business Games

The majority of gaming simulations created to date have been of the business game variety. The usual situation is to have a few teams (normally 2 to 8) competing for a share of a defined economic market. Each team is given some initial resources, and the ways for expanding these resources through coalition and competition are spelled out. The primary objective is to survive and retain the right to play. When survival is not at stake, the objective shifts to maximization of resources or control of the game. Thus, the business game is in many ways similar to the popular parlor game Monopoly (or stated otherwise, Monopoly is a type of business game).

The nice thing about business games—from the analyst's point of view—is that all

51

players have a common objective: survival and then maximization of resources. Thus, it is relatively easy to gauge the success of the various players, and hence deduce clever or high pay-off strategies as a consequence of analyzing the game play. From the players' point of view, the business game teaches the participants how to respond to actions of others and how to anticipate and out-think their competitors. It also can teach valuable lessons in the efficacy of coalition formulation and the "hows" and "whys" of joint actions.

The business game has a theoretical analogue in game theory. The value of game theory was highlighted first by von Neumann and Morgenstern, and has received wide academic attention since then. Its practical use has to date been less pronounced. The game theory construct consists of a number of hypothetical players, each with a series of alternative courses of action, and a payoff matrix corresponding to the respective choices of the players. Thus, in the example below, if player A chooses his action 1 and player B chooses his action 2, A will win $5 and B will lose $3; but, if A chooses his action 2 and B still chooses his action 2, A will win $4 and B will win $1 (Figure 24).

As can be seen in this example, if B chooses his action 1 and A chooses his action 2, both will be better off than for any other choice by either. (This is technically called a "saddle point" of the game.) If an equivalent business game is set up and if it is designed properly, the two players (or teams) should soon realize that it is worth their while to cooperate to maximize their individual rewards.

The results of testing both game theory constructs and business games have been very revealing. They have shown that players do not always behave rationally to maximize their own resources, but tend to be competitive and try to "beat the other guy" regardless of the ultimate rewards to either. Some very interesting notions of behavior have been explored through modifications of business or economic games, and more will no doubt be forthcoming in the next few years.

A modification of the business game, the international game, has received some attention from political scientists. In these latter games, the main resource is "power" and the overriding objective is "control of the political environment." Variations of international games have investigated nuclear disarmament, military coups and economic development.

Figure 24

PAYOFF MATRIX A Vs B	PLAYER B:	
	action B1	action B2
action A1	A:-1; B:-9	A:+5; B:-3
action A2	A: 8; B: 3	A:+4; B:+1
action A3	A:+5; B:-6	A:-3; B:-1

PLAYER A:

Educational Games

Because the best way to think of gaming simulation is as a heuristic or teaching device—where both the gaming participants and the gamer are involved in a mutual learning experience—it seems only natural that gaming simulation should prove useful in the field of education. Our education system is facing the problem of improving simultaneously its quality, coverage, quantity, and minimum standards; and to do so with budgets which are not growing at a pace to match student enrollment. Thus, any innovation which can quickly and cheaply improve the quality and coverage of education is eagerly sought out. Educational games have been considered by many educators to be one of the more promising of these innovations.

Education games can be used to teach students virtually every subject they encounter in elementary and high school. It is not accidental that pre-schoolers teach themselves a great deal about the life around them through the creation of games of make-believe. Most creative adults perform much the same ritual, only less conspicuously. Thus, educational games can be viewed as merely a conscious and systematic application of what children and adults have been doing very effectively, but intuitively and informally, for ages.

The advantages of gaming as educational devices are numerous:

1. *Games are fun* to play—if designed properly, and hence are sources of pleasure to the students.
2. Games allow the student to be an *active participant in the learning experience,* rather than a passive member of an audience.
3. Because the student is immersed in the game and its data and rules, he discovers an *immediacy and relevancy* which often escapes him in books and lectures.
4. The student finds himself *using the data and the rules,* rather than merely hearing about how they can be used.
5. It is *easier to remember* data and information which is used than that which is merely committed to memory
6. Games encourage *intellectual initiative* by yielding game rewards to the innovative student, while penalizing the conservative, unaggressive student.
7. Games require the student to learn how to *organize information* for achieving immediate game objectives.
8. Games encourage *creative and conscientious solutions* to problems.
9. Games teach students how to *communicate* with one another and *work together for mutual gains.*

Some remarkable results have been achieved with educational games aimed at disadvantaged groups. For example, the game of Raid was developed by Clark Abt Associates and played by ghetto youths in Boston aged 13 to 17. The game consisted of the interaction between a team of Police, a team of Protection Racketeers, and three teams representing Citizens of City Blocks. Both the Police and the Racketeers had resources in the form of weapons and men; in addition, the Police had money. The City Block teams had men and money as resources. The objective of the Police was to catch the Racketeers; the Racketeers tried to obtain money and recruit men from City Blocks; and the City Blocks sought to maintain or increase their wealth and their population. The Police and the Racketeers visited (raided) the City Block teams at certain times, but otherwise all communications were written. The players displayed great sophistication in planning strategies. The game was won by the Police.

The game provided seven leadership roles simultaneously. This is rarely achieved in normal classroom activity. Students of low academic achievement at times displayed creative thinking, leadership and verbal expression well beyond their usual performance. Students of widely varying ability worked together effectively on teams, despite the fact that students of lower ability had previously objected to working with the higher ability group. One extremely withdrawn student participated vigorously in the game. The boys were stimulated and performed in both quantity and quality beyond all expectations. Many asked to play the game again, especially some of those of lower achievement. One student commented that the game taught him "how hard it is to be a policeman." Another commented that he had "never concentrated so hard" in his life.

Urban Planning Games

Gaming simulation began to infiltrate into the field of urban planning in the last decade. Articles by Richard Meier and Richard Duke beginning in 1963 appear to be the first public statements of its arrival. The two earliest urban gaming prototypes were 1) the METRO and METROPOLIS series of games developed at the University of Michigan by Richard Duke and 2) the Cornell Land Use Game, usually referred to as CLUG, developed by Allan Feldt at Cornell. The former series of games are based upon a medium-sized metropolitan area (Lansing, Michigan) and the short range decisions facing it with regard to its capital improvements program, tax rate, and elections. Players act out roles of politician, administrator, businessman and educator. METROPOLIS is a smaller and consequently simpler version, whereas METRO is cumbersome, but thorough. Attempts are currently underway to extend these games in a number of directions, such as in the examination of environmental pollution issues. CLUG investigates questions of land development, speculation, and land use control. No specific player roles are assigned. Rather, the game rules govern the options open to the players. These options permit a large area of undeveloped land to be developed through the expenditure of resources.

Among the most ambitious of the urban gaming simulation activities to date are the computer-assisted *Region* and *City* series of games being developed by Envirometrics in Washington, D.C., under the directorship of Peter House. *City 1* illustrates the scope and complexity of these games. Based on a hypothetical metropolitan area of more than 300,000 population, this game simulates the economic and political forces at work.

54

In this game nine teams (three to five members per team) act as entrepreneurs who own economic developments in part of a partially urbanized county which is divided into four political jurisdictions. The playing board contains 625 squares (each square represents one square mile), most of which are unowned at the beginning of play. These land parcels may be purchased and developed by the teams during the course of the game. There are various types of private land use which the teams can develop on a parcel of land: heavy industry, light industry, business goods, personal services, high-income residences, middle-income residences and low-income residences.

Each of the nine teams is elected or appointed by elected officials to assume the duties of one of nine governmental roles: these are played simultaneously with the entrepreneurial functions common to all teams. The elected officials (the county chairman and the central city councilman) must satisfy the electorate (the other teams) in order to stay in office each round. The chairman team appoints other teams to play the roles of the school, public works and safety, highway, planning and zoning, and finance departments. The governmental departments build schools, provide utilities, build and upgrade roads and terminals, maintain roads, buy parkland, zone land, and estimate revenues.

Teams set their own objectives for both the public and private actions they undertake. Team decisions are recorded each round (approximately two hours in length) by a computer, which acts as an accountant and indicates the effects of the teams' actions on one another and on the county itself. The interaction of public and private decisions and their influence over time are illustrated by regularly provided computer printouts. Even though conflicts may develop between urban and suburban interests, among businesses and among governmental departments, teams often find that cooperation is as important as competition in fulfilling their objectives.

The developers of *City 1* have suggested that more sophisticated computer-assisted gaming simulations with the same general structure as *City 1* could be used as 1) educational tools, 2) research vehicles, and 3) aids in policy testing and formulation. However, while *City 1* and other urban games have been played and enjoyed by urban planners and administrators, no city, region, or state government body has as yet committed significant funds toward the development of such a game for its jurisdiction. No major research findings concerning urban structure, technology or behavior have as yet been generated and published. Furthermore, it has yet to be demonstrated that the average low-income citizen participant, who is playing an increasingly significant role in the planning process, can benefit from a gaming experience of the *City 1* type.

The above is not meant as an indictment of *City 1* and similar computerized urban gaming simulations. The importance of such games in furthering our understanding of the urban environment may prove to be substantial. However, it might also be true that these games may be too elaborate and too sophisticated for many of the tasks at which they have been directed. Simpler and more flexible non-computerized games may be more suited to such tasks.

Non-Computerized Urban Gaming Simulation

Urban gamers to date have perhaps spent a disproportionate amount of time perfecting a single or a few related model environments, at the expense of experimentation with a wide range of environments and problem settings. A chief cause for this stems from the speed with which urban gamers have introduced computerization into their activities. Once this "marriage" with the computer has been arranged, much of the freedom and latitude of "bachelorhood" is sacrificed. Once time and money have been invested in a computer program or in a set of programs, the likelihood of changing course in the investigation—of attempting to develop fresh conceptualizations or restructuring research priorities and objectives—is drastically reduced. Too much has been invested to begin anew.

The attractiveness of computerization is alas as compelling as the voice of Lorelei. Urban analysts and theorists have gradually been adopting a more systemic view of the urban environment, in which the various urban components (such as housing, transportation, commercial and industrial centers, population, etc.) are seen as being highly interrelated. The urban environment is viewed as a complex process of interacting subsystems. Simulators of the urban environment have readily adopted the systems approach toward the analysis of the city, and most have consequently sought to integrate as many urban subsystems as possible into their models. Computerization thus became inevitable.

Yet a systems view of the urban environment need not imply *a priori* that all relevant subsystems must be incorporated immediately into the analysis. Individual or small groups of subsystems can be isolated and studied in detail, as long as the analyst keeps in the fore the knowledge that he is treating only a part of a total system. At some point, this partial analysis must be reintegrated into the total systemic framework; and consequently, the linkages essential for reintegration must not be severed and destroyed.

To the extent that computerized urban gaming simulations represent the synthesis of all relevant urban subsystems, their value is significant. However, as vehicles for isolating and focusing on individual subsystems, they thus far have proven to be far too cumbersome and inflexible. Urban subsystems research—particularly in these early stages of inquiry—is highly exploratory in nature. Few accepted theories exist, and knowledge about the various urban components is fragmental and inconclusive. An urban researcher must be prepared to travel down a number of dead-end paths in his search for "laws" and "truths" concerning urban dynamics. He must be willing to retreat and begin afresh. Thus, his tools must be multi-functional and highly flexible. Furthermore, new notions must be capable of being explored and tested quickly and inexpensively, since most will be discarded or at best reformed. Time-consuming and often expensive computerization will usually not be suitable for the task at hand.

However, non-computerized urban gaming simulation—while still for the most part an unexplored art—is potentially a highly valuable research tool. The basic elements of a non-computerized gaming simulation are a scenario, a set of roles, a simulated urban setting, and a list of simple rules governing the interaction of the players with each other and with the game setting. Each of these elements is very flexible and can be modified or extended in relatively short periods of time (in hours or days, depending on the skill of the gamer, his knowledge of the research area, and the complexity of the subject matter). The dynamics of the game play are governed by the strategies and counter-strategies adopted by the game players and by the changes which these strategies bring about on the game setting. All such changes are kept simple; they are usually limited to manual shifts on game board values (simulating land rent, for example), location of player pieces (simulating property ownership, for example), and realignment of power among the various players.

Designing Gaming Simulation

The format used in designing any gaming simulation is to develop first a conceptual framework defining the various player roles, the way these roles interact, and rationale for player decisions. This framework is then formalized and dramatized into a simulation of a life situation. Through repeated tests of the simulation model, refinements are made to correct various awkward elements and distortions.

More specifically, the following types of analysis and creation must take place in the design:

First, it is necessary to formulate the specific decision-making model to be simulated. That is, critical individuals and groups need to be identified and analyzed, both separately and collectively. What the designer should concentrate on is the motivations and aspirations of the identified roles: What are they each trying to do? What stands in their way? What resources do they have? How do they interact with the other groups and individuals? For what purposes?

Specifically, the following general steps in the design process must be performed:

1. *Define the situation to be simulated.* What part of the urban environment is being dealt with? Residential patterns and how they emerge? The election process? Life in the ghetto? Model cities decision making? The growth of railroads in the United States in the last century?
2. *Identify the critical individuals or groups in the situation and their specific roles with respect to the situation.* Who are the players without whom the situation would be clearly incomplete and distorted? (The mayor? The city council? Business interests? The black militant? Ghetto dwellers? The Model Cities director? The white middle class? The hustler? The President? The Congress? Land developers?) What are their respective roles within the situation to be simulated? (To maintain the status quo? To develop a neighborhood? To establish a viable business? To provide funds for renewal?

To operate a social welfare program? To win votes? To dominate the other players through accumulation of resources?)

3. *Identify the initial resources available to each player.* What forms and amounts of resources do each of the players initially control? These might include: Money, goods, services, materials, status, political influence, threat of violence, or information. What will these resources be used for? To buy something? To sell something? To gain control of someone else's resources? To use as bargaining power?

4. *Establish the range and types of transactions which may occur among the players.* Who deals with whom? For what purposes? Are resources exchanged; if so what are the rules governing these exchanges? Are these transactions public (visible to other players) or private (secretly conducted)?

5. *Determine the sequence for these transactions.* Who deals with whom first? What then follows? Are certain transactions contingent upon the occurrence of other transactions; if so, what is the order of these events?

6. *Define how the players use their resources to achieve their target objectives.* What is the ultimate goal or goals of each player? What resources do they need to achieve these? Is it possible for them to acquire this level of resources? How? (Note: it is possible to design a game in which players are assigned objectives which in fact are impossible to achieve. The test is then to discover how quickly this fact is discovered by the player and appropriate adjustments in aspirations or tactics made).

Second, the decision-making model must be translated into a drama or role-playing scenario. The key design problem here is to identify the minimum number of rules required to keep the simulation "on course". Otherwise, the game will become mechanical and player creativity will be stifled.

Specifically, the following must be done:

7. *Select the specific issues or problems on which the simulation is to focus.* The situation selected (and accompanying decision-making model) will no doubt contain within it a wealth of possible issues or problem areas to focus on and dramatize. The game designer should select from these, a small subset of issues and problems characteristic of the entire set which will adequately depict the "flavor" of the overall situation.

8. *Isolate the player roles, player objectives, and resources needed to adequately deal with the selected subset of issues and problems.* That is, reduce and modify the overall decision-model so that it becomes issue-specific. For example, a simulation of the dynamics of integration of formerly all-white residential areas would demand a complex decision-model and require many roles to depict the interplay of societal forces at work. However, limiting the situation to a single black family moving into a specific homogeneous area will greatly reduce the complexity of the simulation and the number of key roles required.

9. *Translate these roles and resources into a series of subplots, events, and character situations which clearly dramatize the key dynamics of the setting*

58

and issues being considered. The degree of sophistication of the dramatization will be governed by the time available to play the game, the number of players, the experience of the players with the roles being simulated, the facilities available, the budget for equipment, and—most importantly—the purpose to be served by the simulation. The overriding rule is to keep the simulation as simple as possible to achieve the stated purpose of the exercise. Little is gained by elaborate scenarios and rules, especially if simpler variations will suffice.

10. *Develop win-lose criteria for the players.* To maintain the momentum of the simulation, each participant should be in a position to assess periodically how well he is doing. Without this feedback, most players will soon lose interest. Accordingly, success criteria should be carefully spelled out and the players should often be given a chance to apply these criteria to their performance to date. The simplest procedure is to have competing players attempt to achieve identical objectives. (This is the mechanism underlying most parlor games, such as Monopoly or Scrabble.). Success can quickly be gauged in such cases by comparing resources or scores. (Note: while this may sound easy, most new game designers have trouble developing adequate win-lose criteria. A good design approach is to test out each role and ask: what do I do now, and why? Appropriate criteria will usually follow directly from the answers to this question.)

Third, the game will need to be refined so that it best serves the intended purpose for it. With experience in game design, these refinements become almost intuitive and there is no need to actually play the game to discover which modifications are most needed. However, the inexperienced game designer will probably need to play out the simulation with live players several times, on each occasion introducing new changes to improve the quality and "playability" of the game.

Specifically, the following general types of refinements should be considered:

11. *Modify the game to make it more or less realistic.* As realism is increased, so is the necessary complexity of individual roles and the number of roles required. It does not generally take too long to reach the stage where a game becomes too complicated to be enjoyed and/or to be educative. Thus, a balance between realism and simplicity must be sought.

12. *Modify the game to make it more or less comprehensive.* There exists a natural temptation to include as much as possible within the game. However, as the number of roles or issues increase, so does the inability to maintain the focus on any specific issue or role. Thus the designer must decide whether to delve deeply into a few roles and issues or more shallowly into a larger set of related roles and issues.

13. *Modify the game to make it more or less melodramatic and tense.* The more conflicts that are introduced into the game roles and the more freedom the players are given to attack openly (verbally) other players, the higher the degree of dramatic tension will be. Yet a point can quickly be reached

59

where the dynamics of specific player encounters overwhelm all other factors to the detriment of the overall flow of the game and its total purpose. Thus, while such encounters should be encouraged if they shed new light or insights on the respective roles, they need to be contained within limits which allow the total simulation to evolve.

The important things to keep in mind are that 1) the gaming simulation should have a minimum number of overriding objectives (such as teaching the participants to appreciate one another's roles); 2) where sacrifices of reality are required, such sacrifices should be avoided where they necessitate compromising the overriding objectives; and 3) the results of the game (winnings and losses of the various players) are less important than the game play itself.

CHAPTER SEVEN

SEVERAL URBAN GAMES

In this chapter a collection of urban gaming simulation models are presented and discussed. These are as follows:

1) LOCO—A prototype game of locational dynamics
2) ECOLOC— A simulation of economic locational processes
3) URBLOC—A simulation of urban spatial processes
4) URBAN POLITICS—A political bargaining game
5) WELFARE—A simulation of the life of a welfare recipient

These games were all designed by the author, with the exception of WELFARE which was designed by Bob Moore and Judy Bremner and modified by the author. They have been selected for presentation here because they collectively depict a wide spectrum of gaming constructs. The first three games focus specifically on the locational behavior of activities in the urban environment. The latter two games are primarily non-spatial in character and deal with a wide range of issues prevalent in the urban environment.

The games are presented in sufficient detail to permit their reproduction and play by the reader. However, to ease the burden on the reader who is more interested in a quick overview of the games, backgrounds and summaries of each game are first presented. Following each description are some notes on the game design and experiences encountered in the actual play of the game.

(1) LOCO:
A prototype game of locational dynamics

BACKGROUND

Any systemic treatment of locational behavior must, at a minimum, involve 1) complementary and competing locational actors and 2) a mechanism for introducing parametric shifts. A minimal urban location game should probably include both economic and social locational actors and some crude form of political process. LOCO is an attempt at such a minimal systemic urban game.

It is what might be referred to as a "nonsense game"; that is, a game dealing with abstract issues rather than "real world" issues. Thus, in LOCO, "red" chases "blue" and political demands include moving "yellow" to other locations. Real world equivalents might have black residential actors moving into an area which is quickly vacated by white residential actors (the urban residential segregation process common to many areas) and political demands for more social services in neglected areas of the city. The major advantage of a "nonsense game" is that fundamental processes can be illuminated and not become clouded among role playing (players getting involved in being say "black militants" and introducing stereotypical behavior learned outside the game) and other types of programmed behavior ("this is the way it *always* is in the real world"). Learning experiences reduced to a fundamental level, even a very simple one such as is employed in LOCO, can have striking effects on participants.

SUMMARY

LOCO has three types of locational actors: Blue, Red and Yellow, each attempting to maximize its relative position on the game board. Blue seeks the lowest value areas; it views the cell values assigned to the 25 cells on the 5x5 game board as representing "land rent". Red seeks the highest value areas; it views these same cell values as constituting "amenity payoffs". However, Blue is a "social climber" and gains bonuses for being near Red. Red, on the other hand, is a "segregationist" who loses points for being near Blue. Yellow attempts to maximize its accessibility to both Red and Blue, but especially the latter; that is, Yellow attempts to locate as close to Blue and Red as possible. Both Red and Blue gain by having Yellow nearby.

In addition, LOCO has a crude political system represented by community representatives and politicians. The community players each have assigned objectives: to see Red, Blue and/or Yellow located in specific areas of the game board. These objectives are conflicting. Each community player has votes (power) which are delegated to a politician or politicians during election periods. Through these votes, the community player hopes to have the game board adjusted (parametric shifts) so that Red, Yellow or Blue will be compelled to locate according to his objective.

The politicians also have objectives assigned to them concerning the desired location of Red, Blue, and/or Yellow. The objectives conflict among the politicians and may also differ from those desired by the community representatives. At election periods, they vie for the votes (power) of the community players. They listen to demands and then each makes a brief "campaign speech". Voting follows. These votes are then used as follows: 1) a single vote can be used by a politician to inflate a single cell value by one unit, say from "6" to "7"; 2) a single vote can be used by a politician to deflate a single cell value by one unit, say from "6" to "5"; 3) a block of three votes can be used to zone a single cell for exclusive use by Red, Blue, and/or Yellow.

The game play follows the following schedule: 1) Five rounds of moves by Red, Yellow and Blue; 2) Voting; 3) Board changes; 4) Three rounds of moves by Red, Yellow and Blue; 5) Voting; 6) Board changes; and 7) Two Rounds of moves by Red, Yellow, and Blue. Thus, the location actors are twice confronted with "parametric shifts" to which they must respond.

GAME DESIGN

LOCO was designed to be played by a minimum of 11 persons, as follows:

    2 – Red
    2 – Blue
    2 – Yellow
    2 – Community Representatives
    3 – Politicians

The number of players can be expanded readily by simply adding additional Yellow, Red and Blue players.

The game was played on a square game board divided into 25 cells in a 5x5 array. Known values ranging from "1" to "6" were assigned to the cells, as follows:

Figure 25

	1	2	3	4	5
A	3	3	5	4	1
B	2	4	6	2	2
C	1	3	6	6	5
D	2	1	4	3	3
E	3	3	3	2	1

Rules for Red Players

Each Red player had five chips. His goal was to earn the most points possible with these chips through strategic locations on the game board. He was in competition against the other red player.

Each Red chip was scored as follows:

1) the value of the cell was earned as points;

63

2) two (2) additional points were earned for each Yellow chip in the same cell;
3) one (1) additional point was earned for each Yellow chip in any neighboring cell (of which there were a maximum of eight);
4) five (5) points were subtracted for each Blue chip in the same cell; and
5) two (2) points were subtracted for each Blue chip in any neighboring cell.

An example of the scoring follows:

Figure 26

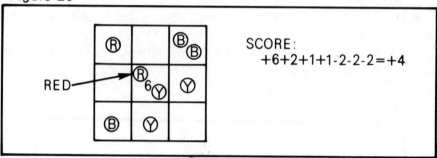

Red players could locate in any of the 25 cells, with the single limitation that no player could locate more than one of his chips in the same cell. The two Red players, however, could both locate one of their chips in the same cell. In round 0, each player placed his five chips on the board. For the next 10 rounds he could move one of his chips to a new location each round. He did not have to make a move if he was happy with his positions.

Points were computed at the end of rounds 5, 8, and 10. The Red player with the highest point total was declared the winner.

Rules for Blue Players

Each Blue player had five chips. His goal was to earn the most points possible with these chips through strategic locations on the game board. He was in competition against the other Blue player.

Each Blue chip was scored as follows:
1) the value of the cell was subtracted as points;
2) three (3) points were earned for each Red chip located in the same cell;
3) one (1) point was earned for each Red chip located in any neighboring cell;
4) two (2) points were earned for each Yellow chip located in the same cell; and
5) one (1) point was earned for each Yellow chip located in any neighboring cell.

An example of the scoring follows. (Figure 27)

Blue players could locate in any of the 25 cells, with the single limitation that no player could locate more than one of his chips in the same cell. The two Blue players, however, could both locate one of their chips in the same cell. In round 0, each player placed his five chips on the board. For the next 10 rounds, he could

64

Figure 27

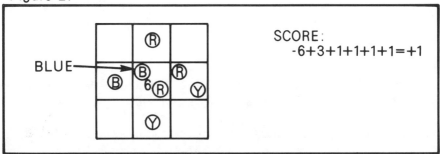

SCORE:
-6+3+1+1+1+1=+1

BLUE

move one of his chips to a new location each round. He did not have to make a move if he was happy with his positions.

Points were computed at the end of rounds 5, 8, and 10. The Blue player with the highest point total was declared the winner.

Rules for Yellow Players

Each Yellow player had three chips. His goal was to earn the most points possible with these chips through strategic locations on the game board. He was in competition against the other Yellow player.

Each Yellow chip was scored as follows:
1) three (3) points were earned for each Blue chip in the same cell;
2) one (1) point was earned for each Blue chip located in a neighboring cell;
3) two (2) points were earned for each Red chip in the same cell; and
4) one (1) point was earned for each Red chip in a neighboring cell.

An example of the scoring follows (Figure 28).

Yellow players could locate in any of the 25 cells, with the single limitation that no player could locate more than one of his chips in the same cell. The two Yellow players, however, could both locate one of their chips in the same cell. In round 0, each player placed his three chips on the board. For the next 10 rounds, he could

Figure 28

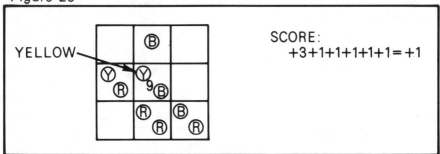

YELLOW

SCORE:
+3+1+1+1+1+1=+1

move one of his chips to a new location each round. He did not have to make a move if he was happy with his positions.

Points were computed at the end of rounds 5, 8, and 10. The Yellow player with the highest point total was declared the winner.

Rules for Community Representatives

Each of the two community representatives had specific targets which they wished to see achieved which were initially known only to them. These were as follows:

1. Representative One wanted to see Blue chips locate in the lower half of the game board (rows D and E). He received two (2) points for each Blue chip in row D or row E after round 8; and three (3) points for each Blue chip in row D or row E after round 10.
2. Representative Two wanted to see Blue chips locate in the upper half of the game board (rows A and B). He received two (2) points for each Blue chip in row A or row B after round 8; and three (3) points for each Blue chip in row A or row B after round 10.

Each representative had 5 units of power (votes) to allocate to politicians. Elections were held after rounds 5 and 8. The election procedure began with each representative stating his demands. The politicians responded with platforms outlining how they would use whatever votes they received. The representatives then cast their votes among the politicians. It was through the voting that the representatives attempted to indirectly accomplish their targets. They could also interact with the politicians during the planning phase following each election.

The representative who earned the highest point total for the two scoring periods was declared the winner.

Rules for Politicians

Each politician was attempting to achieve dual-objectives: 1) to receive as many votes as possible and 2) to attempt to redirect the game board action so as to see specified targets achieved which were known only to him. These targets were as follows:

1. Politician A wanted to see Red chips locate in the left side of the game board (column 1). He received two (2) points for every Red chip in column 1 at the end of round 8; and three (3) points for every Red chip in column 1 at the end of round 10.
2. Politician B wanted to see Red chips locate on the bottom of the game board (row E). He received two (2) points for every Red chip in row E at the end of round 8; and three (3) points for every Red chip in row E at the end of round 10.
3. Politician C wanted to see Yellow chips locate in the top or right side of the game board (row A and column 5). He received two (2) points for every Yellow chip in row A or column 5 at the end of round 8; and three (3) points for every Yellow chip in row A or column 5 at the end of round 10.

Each politician attempted to earn votes from the community representatives during the election periods discussed above. A planning period then followed during which the votes (power) were expended. Three options were open:

1. A politician could use one vote to raise the value of one cell by one point, say from "6" to "7";
2. A politician could use one vote to lower the value of one cell by one point, say from "6" to "5"; or
3. A politician could expend three votes to zone one cell for exclusive use by Red, Blue, and/or Yellow.

The politicians could pool resources or act independently. The politician who received the most votes plus the most additional points for achieving his target was declared the winner.

Schedule of Events

1. *Round 0.* All Red, Yellow, and Blue players simultaneously placed their chips on the game board.
2. *Rounds 1–5.* Each player could move one of his chips per round to a different cell. These moves occurred simultaneously.
3. *Election One:* Community representatives stated their demands. Politicians responded with platforms. Voting then occurred.
4. *Planning Period One:* Discussion was held among the players. The politicians then exercised their options with their assigned power (votes).
5. *Rounds 6–8.* Same as Rounds 1–5 above.
6. *Election Two.* Same as Election One above.
7. *Planning Period Two.* Same as Planning Period One above.
8. *Rounds 9–10.* Same as Rounds 1–5 above.

Sample score sheets used by the various players follow the discussion of LOCO (Figures 29 through 31).

DISCUSSION

As should be clear, LOCO is an easy game to set up and run. Play moves quickly and the 10-round version can easily be fitted into a one-hour period. The two problem areas associated with running the game are as follows: First, the board players (especially Red and Blue) sometimes have trouble calculating their point totals, despite the simple arithmetic involved. Since these calculations are probably at a minimum level for a game of this type and cannot be reduced much without losing some important dynamic, the game controller will have to assume an additional responsibility of assisting players with their calculations. Since there are no secrets among the board players, the players more adept at calculations can help their neighboring players as well. Second, the abstract level at which the game operates may make it difficult for the less articulate (and verbal) players to express demands of politicians or to offer political platforms. In such cases, they can fall back on very simple statements, such as "I want more Red in the upper half of the board."

Figure 29

RED

RULES AND SCORE SHEET

1. You will earn points 3 times, after rounds 5, 8, and 10.
2. You will try to earn more total points than your red opponent.
3. You earn points for *each* of your 5 chips as follows:
   a) you get the value of the cell in which your chip is located;
   b) you get 2 extra points for every Yellow chip in the same cell;
   c) you get 1 extra point for every Yellow chip in one of the surrounding cells;
   d) you *lose* 5 points for every Blue chip in the same cell;
   e) you *lose* 2 points for every Blue chip in one of the surrounding cells.

	ROUND 5	ROUND 8	ROUND 10	
1				
2				
3				
4				
5				GRAND TOTAL
TOTAL				

Figure 30

COMMUNITY REPRESENTATIVE #2

RULES AND SCORE SHEET

1. You want to win more points than the other community spokesman.
2. You receive 2 points for every Blue chip in row D or row E at the end of round 8.
3. You receive 3 points for every Blue chip in row D or row E at the end of round 10.
4. You have 5 votes to give out at each election.

VOTING RECORD

	ELECTION ONE	ELECTION TWO
A		
B		
C		
	5	5

POINTS RECEIVED, ROUND 8 [ ]

POINTS RECEIVED, ROUND 10 [ ]

GRAND TOTAL [ ]

69

Figure 31

POLITICIAN C

RULES AND SCORE SHEET

1. You want to win more points than the other two politicians.
2. You win one point for each vote received in the two elections.
3. You receive 2 points for every Yellow chip in any of the 5 cells in row A or column 5 at the end of round 8.
4. You receive 3 points for every Yellow chip in any of the 5 cells in row A or column 5 at the end of round 10.

ELECTION RESULTS	VOTES FROM #1	VOTES FROM #2	TOTAL VOTES
ELECTION ONE			
ELECTION TWO			

POINTS RECEIVED, ROUND 8 [ ]

POINTS RECEIVED, ROUND 10 [ ]

GRAND TOTAL [ ]

70

As the reader may have noticed, LOCO as presented above is intentionally "loaded." It has been designed with point assignments which will keep blue chasing Red and Yellow chasing Blue indefinitely, unless either (1) a cell value becomes so high (say "15") that it no longer pays Blue to chase Red there or (2) a cell is zoned for Red so that it has an escape area from Blue. This latter option is the cheaper to accomplish since only three votes are required. Thus, the real test of the game for the community players and the politicians is to see if they will be able to glean this fact from the game dynamics and take appropriate action to stabilize the game by strategic zoning of cells for Red's use.

It should be of interest to note that LOCO has been run at several universities during the past year as well as at a conference for high level urban professionals. Yet, only once has a player figured out during the game play that the key lies in zoning cells for Red. And that player was a board player, enacting the role of Red. This sheds some light on the problems students and professionals alike have in thinking systematically. If the entire game dynamics is viewed in its totality (a fairly easy feat to accomplish), the option becomes readily clear. Yet few individuals are geared to viewing things this way; most get caught up in subsystems and in partial dynamics. Thus, the lesson which can be offered from a game as simple as LOCO can be quite dramatic.

(2) ECOLOC:
A simulation of economic locational processes

BACKGROUND

An actor makes a decision to locate a social or economic activity at a given site in the urban area because of his perception of its potential payoff to him (measured in terms of desirability or profitability). The influence of a positive parametric shift on a locale increases the probability of his being attracted to that locale; inversely, the influence of a negative parametric shift on a locale decreases the probability of his being attracted there.

In addition, the presence of new activities of a given social or economic type in a locale may increase the probability that additional activities of this (and related) types will locate there. A primary reason for this is that most locational decisions are imitative in nature, rather than innovative. Rather than attempting to gauge the desirability of all available sites, most locational actors assess the potential payoff of a locale on the basis of their estimates of the payoffs to similar actors already situated at the locale. The consequence is a clear clustering of similar types of activities in favorable locales.

This clustering phenomenon is self-perpetuating. Because of localization and other agglomeration economies, a locale becomes—at least to some optimum level—more desirable for given activity types as the number of units of these and related types increase. Thus, fortuitous locational decisions induce imitation, which

71

in turn induces still more imitation. Through this cumulative process of imitation, the overall distribution of the corresponding activity type (or types) is gradually shifted in the direction of the pioneering fortuitous decisions.

SUMMARY

The purpose of ECOLOC is to simulate the relative propensities of individuals to imitate other decision-makers who have been perceived as having made successive locational decisions. The game focuses on individual players, each of whom has five chips ("establishments") to locate on the game board ("the city"). There are 100 possible squares in which a chip may be located. Each square yields an economic payoff which is revealed to a player only if he locates a chip in that square. It costs the player a certain amount of money to locate in a square and to maintain operations there. Reduced operating costs are realized through agglomeration. The objective of the game for each player is to earn as much money as possible through his locational decisions.

As added elements in the game, randomly-selected squares are determined periodically and their payoffs revealed to all players as "public information." Also, at appropriate points in the game, the game controller introduces some drastic changes on the game board ("parametric shifts") and the players must consequently reconsider their locations in light of these changes. Finally, players are permitted to sell information (payoffs of certain squares) to other players for whatever price can be negotiated.

GAME DESIGN

A relatively simple board game was employed to simulate the above tendencies. The components and features of the game, the game rules and the game instruments were as follows:

Playing Board: The game board consisted of a square board divided into 100 equally-sized blank squares in a 10 x 10 array representing economic space and containing 100 possible locations in which to establish a firm. Values of "1" to "20" inclusively were assigned to the cells in a predetermined, non-random manner known only to the game controller. The values were assigned in such a way that the optimum pattern, when and if discovered by the players, resembled retail land use patterns typical of urban areas (that is, the optimum pattern consisted of a series of centers and subcenters arrayed in clusters and linear extensions). The players were told that "20" was the highest value possible, but were not given any clues as to the distribution of values or if in fact there were squares valued at "20" on the board. Examples of game board values used are depicted on the following pages (Figures 32 through 34).

Players: Four to six persons each with 5 "establishments" (represented by colored poker chips) to locate during the course of the game. Each person was assigned a different color to distinguish his firms from those of the other players. (Numbered chips would have served the same purpose.) Each player began the game with 50 units of financial resources.

72

Figure 32

	1	2	3	4	5	6	7	8	9	10
A	11	3	17	6	5	4	13	10	8	3
B	1	9	14	5	4	4	8	11	12	7
C	12	14	19	3	5	7	5	13	19	16
D	16	5	8	6	2	5	4	4	16	9
E	9	12	3	2	1	14	18	20	8	5
F	2	7	8	1	3	1	9	4	2	6
G	4	8	19	2	18	18	5	6	3	5
H	17	20	14	4	16	13	9	10	7	18
I	15	13	17	6	11	14	2	9	1	13
J	14	9	13	7	9	17	12	6	2	3

**GAME BOARD VALUES
(VARIATION #1)**

Costs and Rewards: It costs 15 units of resources to locate or relocate a firm, and 5 units to maintain it in operation each round. Upon locating in a square, the owner of the firm was told its value privately and credited with that value (as gross revenues) for each round in which the firm remained in that square. Thus, if the cell was valued at "10," it cost the player 20 units for the first round (15 for location and 5 for operation) and 5 units thereafter, and he received a steady round-by-round payoff of 10 units. (Note: an excellent investment, since it is a 33-1/3% first year return on initial investment.) A player could remove one or more chips from

Figure 33

	1	2	3	4	5	6	7	8	9	10
A	4	7	11	10	11	1	2	9	7	6
B	5	10	13	8	4	4	5	6	4	5
C	12	17	12	6	5	3	6	2	2	3
D	8	14	2	2	13	8	1	6	5	1
E	9	8	11	3	20	11	5	4	3	7
F	5	3	8	5	18	14	3	6	10	11
G	8	9	3	6	13	9	7	8	15	12
H	9	5	4	8	6	5	10	14	2	1
I	4	6	5	1	2	7	13	19	13	1
J	3	8	6	4	5	9	8	6	3	2

GAME BOARD VALUES
(VARIATION #2)

the board before any new round began at no cost to him, but also without receiving any payment for investment capital abandoned.

Multiple Occupancy of a Square: A player was permitted to move to a cell currently occupied by himself or by another player or players. It cost 15 units to move into a cell occupied by other players but only 10 units to move into a cell already occupied by that same player (expansion costs rather than initial investment capital). However, for each firm after the first which located in a square, the value of that square for all firms—including the original one—was diminished by

74

Figure 34

	1	2	3	4	5	6	7	8	9	10
A	5	3	1	8	2	1	7	2	5	8
B	8	9	2	5	4	5	6	10	9	3
C	7	4	11	7	3	8	11	6	5	8
D	6	1	14	8	4	7	5	9	2	4
E	1	2	6	5	2	13	11	4	3	1
F	4	16	18	7	3	13	5	3	2	7
G	3	10	20	9	7	15	6	2	5	4
H	5	8	11	3	11	17	19	1	5	2
I	2	6	3	4	2	3	12	7	3	6
J	1	3	2	6	8	10	8	4	8	7

GAME BOARD VALUES
(VARIATION #3)

2 units. Thus, for example, if four firms belonging to one or more players occupied a square initially valued at, say, 16, each of the four firms received a payoff each round of 10 units (16–(2×3)=10) less 5 units for operating expense.

Localization Economies: If four or more adjacent squares were occupied, either by one player or many, the operating cost per round for the firms in these cells was reduced from 5 units to 3 units (Figure 35).

Public Information: After certain rounds determined by the game controller (usually every other round), some information concerning the values of the game

Figure 35

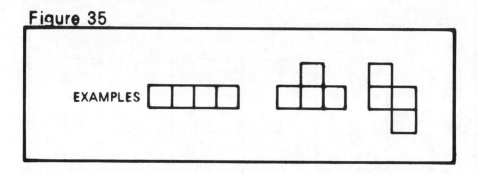

board was revealed to all the players at no cost to them. This was done by selecting a random card from a deck marked 1 to 100 and revealing the value of that square. (For example, if card 75 was drawn, the value of the square in the 8th row, 5th column was revealed to all the players.)

Parametric Shifts: Occasionally, at an appropriate point in the game as determined by the game controller, some public information was revealed which either altered the values of the game board (for example: "all values on the first row are increased by 3 units") or served as an especially revealing clue (for example: "the left center portion of the game board contains a high payoff area"). The choice of the parametric shift which was introduced was left to the discretion of the game controller.

Private Information: After each round private bargaining among the players was permitted. This bargaining was, however, limited to written messages. The messages (requests and responses) were restricted to the following three types:

1. I will pay you _____ units if you tell me the value of cell _____.
2. I will tell you the value of cell _____ if you pay me _____ units.
3. The value of cell _____ is _____ units. Transfer _____ units to me.

Bankruptcy: If during the game play a player's resource position (initial resource units less costs plus revenues) became negative, that player was allowed to continue if he desired. However, his location and expansion costs were increased from 15 and 10 units to 20 and 15 units respectively (reflecting a higher interest rate on capital borrowed.)

Game Play:

1. Each round, the players were given the opportunity to locate or relocate one firm or to pass. All moves were prerecorded on data sheets, along with a short statement outlining the reason for making the move in question. All players then made their moves simultaneously. At the same time, any number of firms could be removed from the game board.
2. After each round, the game controller revealed the value of that square in which the player had located to that player alone.
3. After each round, the players recorded their expenses and revenues, and their current resource position. They were also requested to estimate what their expected revenue per round would be by the conclusion of the game.

4. Negotiations for private information then occurred for a limited period of time or until no more time was required by the players.
5. Public information and/or parametric shifts were introduced before certain rounds at the discretion of the game controller.
6. The game was scheduled for 10 rounds but allowed to expand slightly to allow equilibrium to occur or be approached.
7. The specific objective of the game was not revealed to the players. They could either play for resource maximization or to meet expectation levels.

Game Instrumentation:

1. A cardboard playing board (2 ft. by 2 ft.) divided into 100 identical squares in a 10 x 10 array and labeled 1 to 10 horizontally and A to J vertically.
2. Five colored poker chips for each player.
3. A balance sheet for each player with columns for recording round numbers; moves; expenses, revenues and current resource position; and for estimating expected revenue flow per round by the conclusion of the game.
4. Scratch sheets for use by the players for keeping track of cell values, opposing player moves, and for planning future strategies.
5. A master sheet kept by the controller indicating the value of each square.
6. A deck of 100 cards numbered 1 to 100 for selecting randomly the square whose value was to be revealed as public information.
7. Message pads for sending private information requests and replies.

Samples of the balance sheet and scratch sheet utilized in the game by the players are presented on the following pages (Figures 36 and 37).

DISCUSSION

A wealth of data was generated during the play of ECOLOC. It was possible to retrace the round-by-round moves of each player, identify the reasons for the moves, and plot the player's moves against those of the other players in the game and against his personal expectation levels. Players became increasingly imitative as the game went on, and clusters of chips quickly developed. Parametric shifts were instrumental in causing predictable changes in the pattern of chips on the game board. The higher valued areas of the board were gradually discovered and occupied.

The players themselves seemed to enjoy the game play and were particularly interested in the post-game analysis of results. A few individuals became frustrated as a result of heavy early losses (caused by poor locational choices), but most seemed to find the game challenging and they became increasingly more sophisticated in their play as the game progressed.

One common problem was the inability of most players to keep accurate scoring. Despite the simple arithmetic involved, few individuals kept correct accounts of their revenues throughout. One solution would be to use "play money" so that the actual financial position would be known without the need for computations. However, this would probably prove more cumbersome than its

Figure 36

Round Number	Public Information	Private Information	Move? Yes	Move? No	If Move: From	If Move: To	Reason(s) For Move	Chip Number	Cost of Move	Total Operating Cost	Revenue	Profit or Loss	Total Profit or Loss	Resources at Start	Resources at End of Round	Resource Position Hoped for at End of Game
1								1								
								2								
								3								
								4								
								5								
2								1								
								2								
								3								
								4								
								5								
3								1								
								2								
								3								
								4								
								5								

Name   Date   Player Code

PLAYER SCORE SHEET

78

Figure 37

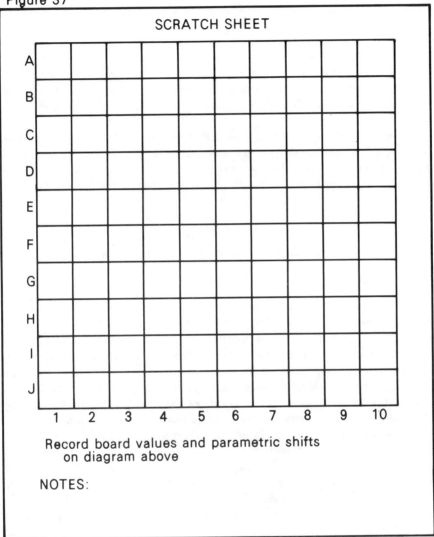

SCRATCH SHEET

Record board values and parametric shifts
on diagram above

NOTES:

worth. Alternatively, players could be assigned less chips to manage, but this would greatly reduce the challenge of the game. Since the win-loss picture is really of secondary importance anyway, the best solution would probably be to keep the game as it is and anticipate scoring errors.

From the game controller's position, this game is very easy to set up and run. The only cumbersome part is walking around each round and revealing to each player in secret the payoff value of any new square occupied. There is no simple way to avoid this. One solution would be to give each player a sheet with the payoffs hidden behind peel-off labels. They could then discover the new values themselves. Alternatively, an assistant could be used to help reveal new values to the players and thus speed up the process.

A more sophisticated version of ECOLOC might include heterogeneous economic actors representing different activity types. Each player would then play against his own unknown set of payoff values, which would be interrelated appropriately with those of complementary activities. Thus, while the player could receive insights from watching the movement of other players, these insights would be more subtle.

Another variation might be to have action stop while the players themselves decided which parametric shifts to introduce. They would be expected to pay the cost of implementing these changes ("tax payments"). This variation might afford some interesting insights into cooperative behavior among competing players.

(3) URBLOC:
A simulation of urban spatial processes

BACKGROUND

Most locational decisions in the urban environment are made by individual decision-making units (heads of households, businessmen, corporations, etc.). In all cases such decisions are made to enhance the relative position of the decision-making unit (through increased satisfaction or economic profit, or both). However, these positions are also affected by decisions beyond the direct control of the individual decision-making unit—those made through the political system. Accordingly, to the extent possible, these individual units will try to influence these political decisions. This is most often accomplished through the ballot box.

The political decision-makers, in turn, are attempting to base their decisions on their perceived notions of what it is their constituencies need and want. Being individuals, they are also likely to have personal goals which differ to some extent from those expressed by their constituencies. Through their political decisions, they attempt to influence the decisions of the individual units so that the resultant pattern of locations will be consistent with their goals and those of their constituencies.

SUMMARY

The purpose of URBLOC is to examine the relationships existing among priming actors and secondary actors. URBLOC is an advanced version of ECOLOC. The number of board roles is expanded from basically one to four distinct role types (economic actors, upper income residents, middle income residents, and lower income residents). Within these role types further differentiation of roles was achieved by creating personalized objectives to be sought during the game play. A total of 16 particular roles were created for the game (four for each role type).

80

Each of the players was given 5 chips to locate on a playing board similar to that used in ECOLOC. In ECOLOC, all players dealt with the same unknown payoff matrix, in URBLOC there were different payoffs for each of the four role types. Each player had a dual objective of earning the most points from the location of his chips, and extra points for having a hidden objective realized.

Superimposed upon the game board was a political game. Specifically, 6 individuals were assigned roles as politicians. Their respective ideologies were predetermined and covered the total political spectrum. Their objective was to win votes during election periods and utilize these to alter the game board payoffs through the placement of "bonus chips" on the board (equivalent to "parametric shifts"). They each vied for the votes of the 16 board players, and in addition had hidden objectives which they attempted to attain during the course of the game. Their relative share of the total votes cast determined how influential a role they would have in spending the authorized budget of bonus chips.

As an added feature, the four board players depicting low income residents could cast votes into a "riot box." If sufficient number of votes accumulated, a "riot" occurred. This had the effect of wiping out part of the budget.

Game Design

URBLOC was a relatively simple game designed to portray a political process in a typical urban community. The game focused on spatial issues; that is, the players' actions and rewards were centered around the location of chips on the game board.

Types of Player Roles: There were two general types of players in the game: the community players (those who placed chips on the game board) and the politicians (those who altered the values on the game board by their decisions). Roles within these two general types were further broken down as follows:

Community Players	*Politicians*
upper income residents	conservatives
middle income residents	moderates
lower income residents	liberals
economic actors	radicals

Specifically, the game as originally designed had 22 roles, including 16 community players and 6 politicians.

The Game Board. The game board was divided into 100 cells, each having unknown payoffs for the various community players. For example, cell C10 paid 0 points for every upper income chip located there, +5 points for every middle income chip located there, −2 points for every low income chip located there, and +5 points for every economic chip located there. The values used are presented on the following pages (Figures 38 through 41).

Rules for Community Players: Each community player was assigned 5 chips. These were color-coded and numbered for easy identification. These chips could be located on any of the 100 cells on the game board, with the single exception that

81

Figure 38

	1	2	3	4	5	6	7	8	9	10
A	0	0	0	0	0	0	0	0	0	0
B	0	5	0	0	5	5	-5	-5	-5	5
C	10	20	5	0	0	0	-5	15	0	5
D	5	15	15	5	0	5	10	25	10	0
E	0	5	0	0	0	0	20	30	15	0
F	0	0	0	0	0	0	15	20	5	0
G	10	10	0	5	10	15	25	0	0	0
H	20	25	0	0	0	0	0	0	15	0
I	5	15	0	0	5	5	10	15	20	10
J	0	0	0	0	0	0	0	0	5	5

BOARD VALUES
(ECONOMIC PLAYERS)

no player could locate more than one of his chips on the same cell. (A player was allowed to locate one of his chips in a cell containing a chip of a rival player.) For each round in which a chip was located in a given cell, the player received the value of that cell as his payoff (economic or social profit) for that chip. Upon locating in a cell, the value of that cell was revealed to that player alone.

At the start of the game, the chips of the various players were placed on the game board by the game controller. These selections were made to insure that each

Figure 39

	1	2	3	4	5	6	7	8	9	10
A	-5	-3	-1	1	0	1	1	5	2	2
B	-5	-3	1	4	3	1	2	3	5	0
C	-10	0	-1	2	4	5	3	0	3	-2
D	-10	0	0	-1	5	3	2	0	3	1
E	-10	-10	-5	-2	0	5	0	0	0	2
F	-2	-2	-2	-2	-2	0	0	0	-1	4
G	-2	0	-10	-10	-10	-10	-1	-1	-1	-1
H	0	0	-4	-4	-2	-2	-10	-10	0	-3
I	-5	0	-10	-4	-2	-4	-10	0	0	-5
J	-10	-10	-10	-5	-5	-10	-10	-10	-5	-5

BOARD VALUES
(LOW INCOME PLAYERS)

chip would initially have a positive payoff. The payoffs were not, however, the best that the players could do. Each round, the players were permitted to change the location of *one* chip if they so desired. The object of the game for the community players was to earn as many points as possible by the end of the game (round 20). The initial locations are illustrated on a chart which follows (Figure 42).

In addition to the points earned from the cells in which their chips were located, community players could earn extra points in two ways: 1) by being in the same

83

Figure 40

	1	2	3	4	5	6	7	8	9	10
A	6	7	3	4	5	3	2	-1	-3	-1
B	8	8	4	-2	-5	-7	-10	-5	-2	3
C	2	0	5	3	-4	-10	-5	0	-3	5
D	0	0	0	5	-2	-5	-3	0	-2	4
E	1	2	4	7	4	-1	0	0	0	-2
F	3	5	5	4	7	6	0	0	4	-1
G	6	8	2	1	2	0	0	5	6	6
H	0	0	5	8	5	4	1	2	0	4
I	4	0	2	8	7	8	0	0	0	4
J	0	0	0	4	5	2	0	0	4	3

BOARD VALUES
(MIDDLE INCOME PLAYERS)

cells or in one of the surrounding cells of the cells which contained bonus chips (how bonus chips were placed on the board is explained below) and 2) by achieving personal objectives (as explained below and on individual game role sheets).

Control of Political Power by Community Players: Each community player had assigned to him some units of political power which he utilized during elections to delegate power to his chosen candidate or candidates among the political players. This political power was distributed as follows:

Figure 41

	1	2	3	4	5	6	7	8	9	10
A	0	0	0	0	0	0	0	-5	-10	-5
B	2	0	0	-5	-15	-10	-10	-5	-10	-5
C	5	0	0	0	-10	-10	-5	0	-5	0
D	8	0	0	0	-5	-10	-5	0	-5	0
E	9	6	3	1	0	-5	0	0	0	-5
F	4	1	5	2	4	0	0	0	0	-5
G	1	3	8	10	8	0	0	2	1	0
H	0	0	0	0	1	3	7	5	0	1
I	0	0	5	2	1	4	9	0	0	3
J	6	10	7	4	2	7	10	8	3	1

BOARD VALUES
(UPPER INCOME PLAYERS)

low income players jointly control	25 units
middle income players jointly control	25 units
upper income players jointly control	25 units
economic actors jointly control	25 units
Total	100 units

In the game as run with 16 community players (4 in each role), power was

Figure 42

INITIAL LOCATION OF CHIPS

ECONOMIC (RED)

1. B6	6. I10	11. G6	16. I8
2. H9	7. B10	12. I7	17. I9
3. B5	8. H2	13. J10	18. B2
4. B2	9. C10	14. I5	19. E9
5. E8	10. D3	15. D8	20. I5

LOW INCOME (BLUE)

1. F10	6. D6	11. C5	16. E10
2. B4	7. C4	12. A8	17. A4
3. A9	8. A8	13. B7	18. D5
4. B7	9. E10	14. B3	19. C6
5. D6	10. D9	15. D6	20. A10

MIDDLE INCOME (YELLOW)

1. G1	6. B10	11. B1	16. C3
2. J6	7. I4	12. H6	17. E3
3. F5	8. E4	13. C3	18. I10
4. F4	9. H7	14. E1	19. I1
5. J10	10. C4	15. E3	20. A5

UPPER INCOME (WHITE)

1. C1	6. E2	11. F1	16. G3
2. I5	7. J5	12. J1	17. I4
3. J1	8. F5	13. E2	18. C1
4. I3	9. I6	14. F4	19. E3
5. J4	10. H8	15. H6	20. J9

distributed among the players evenly. Thus, three players in each role received 6 units of power, and the fourth player received 7 units of power.

Rules for Politicians: The political players were initially assigned equal amounts of power. Thus, in the game as run with six politicians, four players initially received 17 units of power and two players initially received 16 units of power. The total 100 units of power were redistributed during elections according to the votes of the community players. Such elections were held every five rounds, taking place before rounds 6, 11, 16, etc.

With these power units, the political players attempted to spend all or part of their 5-round budgets. These budgets could only be spent on locating bonus chips on the game board in whatever cells the political players could agree upon.

At the start of the game and immediately following elections, the political players were given a budget of 10 millobucks to spend within a five-round period. *Budget surpluses* (millobucks not spent during the 5 rounds) *were not carried over to the next period.* The budget could be spent as follows:

a. Each *residential service bundle bonus chip* cost 1 millobuck and increased the residential points in the cell in which it was placed and in the 8 surrounding cells by +3 points. (Examples of residential service bundle bonus chips might be improved neighborhood parks, lighting, sewage and waste disposal service, schools, roads, and health facilities.)

b. Each *economic area improvement bonus chip* cost 5 millobucks and increased the economic points in the cell in which it was placed and in the 8 surrounding cells by +15 points. (Examples of economic area improvement bonus chips might include downtown lighting and tree planting, public parking garages, industrial park development, and improved shopper transportation services.)

c. Each *special project bonus chip* cost the entire budget of the 5-round period (i.e. 10 millobucks). There were three types of special projects which could be implemented.

1) *New sports complex:* This is a multi-structured complex, including a football stadium and an arena, and requiring extensive parking facilities and access routes. It could be located anywhere on the game board. Each economic player would receive a bonus of 50 points (in addition to the board points) for locating one of his chips in the same cell or in one of the eight surrounding cells to the complex site. *Only one bonus could be earned by any player.* The complex development had adverse effects on residences: the residential values of the cell in which the complex was located and the eight surrounding cells were decreased by 10 units for the remainder of the game.

2) *Public rapid transit system:* The system is linear or zig-zag covering nine contiguous cells anywhere on the game board. It had the effect of increasing the economic value of the nine cells along the route by 25 units each and all the residential values along the route by 5 units each.

3) *Elevated express highway:* This is a linear or zig-zag system of nine contiguous cells anywhere on the game board. It benefitted the population at both ends, but detracted from the residential value of the areas through which it passed. It had the effect of increasing the residential value of the two end cells and the ten peripheral surrounding cells (five around each of the two end cells) by 5 units and the economic value of these same 14 cells by 25 units. Furthermore, it depressed all the residential values of the seven cells along the route but not end cells by 10 units each.

In order to spend all or part of the budget, the political players had to accumulate at least 60 power units in favor of the action. This was accomplished in the following manner: A political player recommended some action for discussion and voting. Discussion occurred followed by a hand vote. The political players could use all or part of their assigned power units in the vote. If at least 60 votes were in favor of the action, it carried, and was immediately enacted. The bonus chips were marked for easy identification.

The objective of the game for the political players was to earn as many power units as possible during the elections held each 5 rounds. In addition, the players could earn additional "success points" by achieving certain political objectives known only to them (and explained below and on the individual game role sheets).

Election Procedure: An election took place every 5 rounds, beginning before round 6. Each of the community players introduced himself, revealed the number of power units he controlled, and stated his demands of the political players to secure his vote.

The political players then responded by introducing themselves, revealing the number of power units they presently were assigned, describing past performance, and listing their promises if given votes. (They were free to slander their fellow political players if they were so inclined.) The community players then delegated in turn their power units to one or more political players for use during the next 5 rounds (that is, if a player had 6 power units to assign, he could give all 6 to one player; 2 to one player and 4 to another; etc.).

The low income players had a further option open to them. If they did not wish to support any political player, they could assign their votes to the "riot box." They were also at liberty to assign part of their political units to one or more political players and part to the "riot box."

Rules Governing Riots: When at least 20 power units had accumulated in the "riot box," a "riot" occurred as soon as the low income players could demonstrate that a majority of them favored a "riot."

The consequence of a "riot" was that 3 millobucks from the current budget were turned over to the low income players for use as they saw fit, and 2 additional millobucks were lost from the total budget for the next 5 rounds (to represent a city-wide economic and social loss as a result of the riot). The low income players had to have a majority consensus among themselves (that is, at least 13 power units of the 25 held jointly by these players) before they could spend these 3 millobucks.

Specific Player Objectives: In addition to the general game objectives as stated above, both the community players and the political players attempted to achieve specific objectives given during the game play (Figures 44 through 65). Examples of these follow:

1. Upper income resident A loses 2 points for every middle income chip located in the same cell or in the next cell to any one of his chips. Thus his specific objective is to "stay clear" of middle income chips.
2. Lower income resident B is anxious to move into a middle class area. This is expressed by his winning 2 bonus points for every middle class chip in the same cell or next to one of his chips.
3. Conservative political player C wishes to maintain the status quo. That is, he

88

wants to see the low income chips kept out of middle income areas. He loses 4 "success units" for every low income chip in the same cell as a middle income chip.

4. Radical political player D wishes to disrupt the political process. He receives 1 "success unit" for every millobuck not spent plus 5 "success units" for every riot occurring.

A complete set of player roles is offered below.

Time and Player Requirements: Each round lasted for no more than 5 minutes. Between 15 and 20 minutes were reserved for each election. Thus, three hours in total was needed to explain the rules and play a complete game of 20 rounds. It was highly desirable for players to participate in URBLOC at least twice, once in a community player role and once in a political player role.

A minimum of 12 players were needed to play the complete game (2 in each of the 4 community roles plus 4 politicians), plus two game controllers. As many as 28 players could be accommodated with a recommended distribution being 2 players for each of the six political roles and 4 players for each of the community roles.

The game room configuration utilized was as follows (Figure 43):

Sample score sheets for URBLOC are presented in Figures 66 through 70 following the description of the 22 roles.

DISCUSSION

As should be apparent from the materials above, URBLOC is a far more sophisticated game than either ECOLOC or LOCO. Contained within it—in varying levels of realism—are most of the dynamics found within the urban environment. This particular game has been very well received by students and professionals alike who have played it. It generally results in a very lively discussion during which

Figure 43

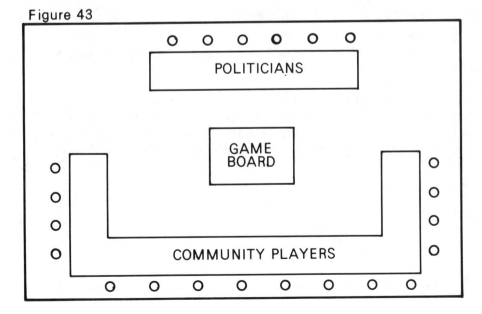

many suggestions are offered for further improving the realism of the game. This is excellent, in that one major objective of any gaming exercise is to stimulate the participants to reach out for a next-generation version of the game in question.

The actual play of the game is generally lively and fast-moving. Players become increasingly more willing to pool power in order to gain control of the game's resources—the budget. They also learn to appreciate more fully the relationships existing between the political system and social and economic locational processes.

Because of the large number of players, at least two game controllers are required to keep the game moving at a good pace. The major delay factor, as with ECOLOC, is the identification of payoff values for new locations. It is also useful to select a few players who are known to be articulate to speak first during the elections, as both community players and political players, to encourage others to "open up" and expand upon their demands or campaign promises when their turns come up later.

URBLOC can readily be adapted to fit most existing political structures, and the hidden board values can be selected to simulate—at least in a rough fashion—any urban area. As such, the series is potentially very useful as an educative tool.

22 GAME ROLES
(Figures 44 through 65)

Figure 44

INDIVIDUAL GAME ROLE

Player: Economic (red), chips 1—5

Common Objective: Maximize value of your 5 chips by the end of the game (round 20)

Personal Objective: You are the owner of a chain of low-cost shoe stores located throughout the city. Your principal customers are low-income persons. Thus, to maximize your sales you should be located as close to the low-income population as possible.

You receive 10 bonus points for every low-income chip sharing a cell with one of your chips at the conclusion of the game (round 20). However, should a "riot" occur during the course of the game, deduct 100 points from your score.

90

Figure 45

```
┌─────────────────────────────────────────────────────────────┐
│                    INDIVIDUAL GAME ROLE                       │
│                                                               │
│  Player:     Economic (red), chips 6—10                       │
│  Common                                                       │
│  Objective:  Maximize value of your 5 chips by the end of the game │
│              (round 20)                                       │
│  Personal                                                     │
│  Objective:  Besides owning several commercial establishments through- │
│              out the city, you have considerable money tied up in real │
│              estate. You have two projects which you would like to see │
│              developed to maximize the gains from this land.  │
│                                                               │
│              (1) You would like to see a sports complex developed in │
│                  B8. You receive 150 bonus points if this development │
│                  occurs during the course of the game.        │
│                                                               │
│              (2) You would like to see a rapid transit system con- │
│                  structed in a north-south direction through the │
│                  columns 7 and 8 corridor. If such a system is │
│                  developed, you receive 100 bonus points.     │
└─────────────────────────────────────────────────────────────┘
```

Figure 46

```
┌─────────────────────────────────────────────────────────────┐
│                    INDIVIDUAL GAME ROLE                       │
│                                                               │
│  Player:     Economic (red), chips 11—15                      │
│  Common                                                       │
│  Objective:  Maximize value of your 5 chips by the end of the game │
│              (round 20).                                      │
│  Personal                                                     │
│  Objective:  You are the owner of a chain of clothing stores located at │
│              various points in the eastern half of the city. You are │
│              anxious to maintain your sales position by continuing to │
│              serve the populations living in the western part of the city │
│              who are increasingly utilizing the more western centers. │
│              You feel that better transportation from west to east will │
│              be required to accomplish this.                  │
│                                                               │
│              You receive 100 bonus points if an east-west rapid transit │
│              system is developed in the city, and 150 bonus points if an │
│              east-west elevated express highway is constructed. │
└─────────────────────────────────────────────────────────────┘
```

91

Figure 47

INDIVIDUAL GAME ROLE

Player: Economic (red), chips 16-20

Common
Objective: Maximize value of your 5 chips by the end of the game (round 20).

Personal
Objective: You fear that the commercial areas of the city will continue to lose their market to the new suburban centers unless major expenditures are made throughout the city to improve the appearance of the commercial areas.

You receive 30 bonus points for every economic area improvement bonus chip which is located on the game board by the politicians during the course of the game.

Figure 48

INDIVIDUAL GAME ROLE

Player: Low Income (blue), chips 1—5

Common
Objective: Maximize value of your 5 chips by the end of the game (round 20).

Personal
Objective: As a result of a past riot, the commercial activity in cells B8 and B7 has greatly deteriorated. As a concerned neighborhood leader, you are interested in bringing commerce back to this area.

You receive 25 bonus points for each economic chip (red) which is located in either cell B7 or B8 at the end of the game (round 20).

Figure 49

INDIVIDUAL GAME ROLE

Player: Low Income (blue), chips 6−10

Common Objective: Maximize value of your 5 chips by the end of the game (round 20).

Personal Objective: You are working hard to improve the quality of residential life for low income persons.

You receive 10 bonus points for each *residential service bundle bonus chip* located in cells B6, B7, B8, B9, C6, or C7 at the end of the game (round 20).

Figure 50

INDIVIDUAL GAME ROLE

Player: Low Income (blue), chips 11−15

Common Objective: Maximize value of your 5 chips by the end of the game (round 20).

Personal Objective: You are a young radical who feels the best political tactic is to paralyze the political process. You are especially incensed when your fellow low-income players participate in the process.

Your strategy is to discourage the other low-income players from supporting any of the political players by attacking each of them during the elections. You receive 5 bonus points for every vote other than your own which is placed in the riot box.

Figure 51

INDIVIDUAL GAME ROLE

Player: Low income (blue), chips 16—20

Common Objective: Maximize value of your 5 chips by the end of the game (round 20).

Personal Objective: You feel that a rapid transit system is needed to connect the low-income area of the city to the commercial center.

You receive 100 bonus points if a rapid transit system is developed which roughly follows the route: B4-B5-B6-B7-B8-C8-D8-E8-F8.

Figure 52

INDIVIDUAL GAME ROLE

Player: Middle Income (yellow), chips 1—5

Common Objective: Maximize value of your 5 chips by the end of the game (round 20).

Personal Objective: You represent the liberal elements of the community who are interested in encouraging balanced neighborhoods containing both middle and low income elements. Your strategy is to enhance the value (residential) of the "fringe areas" and hence encourage the occupancy of these areas by a mix of residential players.

You receive 5 bonus points for each *residential service bundle bonus chip* placed in either cells A6, A7, B3, C4, or D10 by the end of the game (round 20).

94

Figure 53

INDIVIDUAL GAME ROLE

Player: Middle Income (yellow), chips 6−10

Common
Objective: Maximize value of your 5 chips by the end of the game (round 20).

Personal
Objective: You own a small department store in cell G5 and would be happy to see more economic activity in that area.

        You receive 10 bonus points for every economic (red) chip located in or around cell G5 by the conclusion of the game (round 20).

Figure 54

INDIVIDUAL GAME ROLE

Player: Middle Income (yellow), chips 11-15

Common
Objective: Maximize value of your 5 chips by the end of the game (round 20).

Personal
Objective: You feel that an elevated express highway should be constructed to connect the northwest corner of the city to the city center (located around E8).

        You receive 100 bonus points if an express highway is constructed which roughly follows the route: B2-B3-B4-B5-B6-B7-B8-C8-D8.

95

Figure 55

INDIVIDUAL GAME ROLE

Player: Middle Income (yellow), chips 16--20

**Common
Objective:**   Maximize value of your 5 chips by the end of the game (round 20).

**Personal
Objective:**   You represent the suburbanite element of the community interested in enhancing the residential value of the outlying areas of the city. You receive 5 bonus points for each *residential service bundle bonus chip* located by the politicians along any of the four edges of the game board (rows A and J, columns 1 and 10) by the end of the game (round 20).

Figure 56

INDIVIDUAL GAME ROLE

Player: Upper Income (white), chips 1—5

**Common
Objective:**   Maximize value of your 5 chips by the end of the game (round 20).

**Personal
Objective:**   You are the owner of the city's professional football team and are anxious to see a new sports complex built. You prefer cell A8 for the location of the stadium, but will settle for other reasonable locations.

You receive 200 bonus points if the sports complex is located in cell A8 and 150 bonus points for any other location on the game board.

Figure 57

INDIVIDUAL GAME ROLE

Player: Upper Income (white), chips 6–10

Common
Objective: Maximize value of your 5 chips by the end of the game (round 20).

Personal
Objective: You are appalled at the low quality of residential services in the city. You feel that too much emphasis has been placed on improving the commercial areas and in support of large scale projects, such as sports complexes.

You receive 10 bonus points for each *residential service bundle bonus chip* placed on the game board by the end of the game (round 20), but *lose* 20 bonus points for each *economic area improvement bonus chip* and 100 bonus points for each special project developed on the board.

Figure 58

INDIVIDUAL GAME ROLE

Player: Upper Income (white), chips 11–15

Common
Objective: Maximize value of your 5 chips by the end of the game (round 20).

Personal
Objective: As a child, you lived in cell B8 which was then a nice middle class area. It has now become the heart of the slum, and you are saddened by this change. You are actively involved in renewing this area.

You receive 100 bonus points for every *economic area improvement bonus chip* located in cell B8 and 25 bonus points for every *residential service bundle bonus chip* located there by the end of the game (round 20).

Figure 59

INDIVIDUAL GAME ROLE

Player: Upper Income (white), chips 16–20

Common Objective: Maximize value of your 5 chips by the end of the game (round 20).

Personal Objective: Your brother-in-law is Politician 1. Without letting the other players know this, attempt to influence their votes for him during the elections. (He is a moderate interested in appealing to a wide cross-section of voters.)

You receive 1 bonus point for every vote *other than your own* which is cast for Politician 1 during the three elections held before rounds 6, 11, and 16.

Figure 60

INDIVIDUAL GAME ROLE

Player: Politician 1

Common Objective: Maximize number of votes received.

Personal Objective: You are a moderate member of the city council. Your aim is to appeal to a wide cross-section of voters.

You receive 50 bonus points for each of the three elections in which you receive at least one vote from each of the four types of community players (i.e., at least one vote from one of the economic players, at least one vote from one of the high income players, at least one vote from one of the middle income players, and at least one vote from one of the low income players).

Figure 61

INDIVIDUAL GAME ROLE

Player: Politician 2

Common
Objective: Maximize number of votes received.

Personal
Objective: You are a liberal member of the city council. You are
            unhappy about the slowness with which the council acts
            and its inability to substantially improve conditions in the
            low income area. Yet you believe in the political process.

            You gain 20 bonus points for all political decisions which
            positively influence the value of low income (blue) chips on
            the game board (i.e., for the location of residential service
            bundle bonus chips in predominantly low income areas).
            However, you *lose* 50 bonus points if a riot occurs.

Figure 62

INDIVIDUAL GAME ROLE

Player: Politician 3

Common
Objective: Maximize number of votes received.

Personal
Objective: You are the radical member of the city council. You gain
            delight in causing confusion and inaction in political
            bargaining sessions.

            You receive 5 success points for every millobuck *not* spent
            by the politicians. You also receive 25 success points for
            each riot which occurs.

Figure 63

INDIVIDUAL GAME ROLE

Player: Politician 4

Common Objective: Maximize number of votes received.

Personal Objective: You are the most conservative member of the city council. You feel that too much money has already been spent in low income areas and are against further spending of this sort. You favor the construction of a new sports stadium complex in the right corner of the game board.

You receive 100 bonus points if a sports complex is located in the northeast quarter of the board. You *lose* 10 bonus points for each residential service bundle bonus chip located in a cell containing a low income chip.

Figure 64

INDIVIDUAL GAME ROLE

Player: Politician 5

Common Objective: Maximize number of votes received.

Personal Objective: You are a conservative businessman. You own some property in the southeast corner of the city and are eager to see commercial development occur there.

You receive 25 bonus points for every economic area improvement bonus chip located in cells I9, I10, J9, or J10.

In addition, you receive 150 bonus points if either a rapid transit system or an elevated express highway is developed which goes to cell I9.

Figure 65

INDIVIDUAL GAME ROLE

Player: Politician 6

**Common
Objective:** Maximize number of votes received.

**Personal
Objective:** You owe political debts to the middle income player (yellow) with chips 6 through 10 and to the upper income player (white) with chips 6 through 10. Your aim is to pay them back by increasing the board value of their chips.

You receive 10 bonus points for every residential service bundle bonus chip which is located in the same cell as yellow chips 6 through 10 or white chips 6 through 10.

Figure 66

Community Player Ballot Form

Player Role

Political Power To Allocate

Name

Date

Allocation of Political Power to Politicians

Election Round	List of Demands as Read to Politicians (Example: I Want Residential Service Bundle Bonus Chips in Cells A5 and F3)	Allocation of Political Power to Politicians
6		Politician 1 Politician 2 Politician 3 Politician 4 Politician 5 Politician 6 Riot Box (low income only)
11		Politician 1 Politician 2 Politician 3 Politician 4 Politician 5 Politician 6 Riot Box (low income only)
16		Politician 1 Politician 2 Politician 3 Politician 4 Politician 5 Politician 6 Riot Box (low income only)

Figure 67

| Community Player Data Sheet | | | | | | | | | | Name | | |
| Player Role   LOW INCOME, 16-20 | | | | | | | | | | Date   SAMPLE | | |

Round No.	Location of Chips					Points Earned for Chips					Change in Total Points	Total Points
	16	17	18	19	20	16	17	18	19	20		
Start	A5	C6	F10	G1	G2	3	1	8	2	5		19
1		A1					-2				-3	16
2		F9					2				4	20
3				H2					-3		-5	15
4				F8					1		4	19
5				J3					7		6	25
6		J2					4				2	27
7		NO MOVE									0	27
8		NO MOVE					7		10		6	33
9	J4					5					2	35
10		NO MOVE									0	35
11		NO MOVE									0	35
12		NO MOVE								-5	-10	25
13					I4					2	7	32
14					I2					5	3	35
15		NO MOVE									0	35
16		NO MOVE									0	35
17		NO MOVE									0	35
18		NO MOVE									0	35
19					A5						6	1	36
20		NO MOVE									0	36

Bonus Points Earned 10+10 -25=   BONUS TOTAL -5
(for achieving individual game
role objective)   GRAND TOTAL 31

103

Figure 68

Political Player Voting Sheet

Player Role

Name

Date

Action Submitted for Vote	Round No.	Sub-mitted By	Check One		Power Units
			for	agnst	

Figure 69

Political Player Election Record			Name
Player Role			Date

Election Round	Notes of Demands as Stated by Community Players	Platform as Read to Community Players	Votes Received
6			
11			
16			

TOTAL VOTES RECEIVED

Bonus Points Earned
(for achieving individual game role objective)   = TOTAL BONUS POINTS

GRAND TOTAL

Figure 70

LOW INCOME, 16-20

SCRATCH SHEET

SAMPLE

for recording
board values
and location
of bonus chips

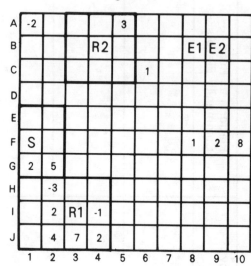

notes:

    R1 = residential bonus after round 7

    R2 = residential bonus after round 18

     S = sports stadium, residential down by 10
       after round 11

BONUS POINTS

gain 10 bonus points for economic bonus
in B8 (E1) in round 3

gain 10 bonus points for economic bonus
in B9 (E2) in round 9

lose 25 bonus points for sports stadium
construction in round 11

(4) URBAN POLITICS:
A political bargaining game

BACKGROUND

Much of the dynamics of the urban environment does not focus on individual location decisions of small economic and social units as has been depicted above in LOCO, ECOLOC, and URBLOC. Rather, the positions of the actors are fixed and the interplay focuses on improving conditions within the locations occupied. Thus, instead of someone moving where the amenities (schools, parks, better roads, etc.) are, that individual may remain fixed in his location but demand more and better amenities in his neighborhood.

URBAN POLITICS represents a transition from location games to their non-locational counterparts. This is not to imply that no locational considerations are involved in these latter games. Instead what is suggested is that the emphasis shifts from movement to improvement, from seeking better locations to making current locations better.

URBAN POLITICS was designed specifically to demonstrate the plight of low income people when attempting to operate within the political system. The game focuses on "political power" and upon how this power can be mobilized to achieve given objectives.

SUMMARY

The basic design of URBAN POLITICS is identical with that utilized in the "election" components of LOCO and URBLOC; namely, a repetitive sequence of:
1) community demands
2) political platforms
3) voting
4) budget spending/coalition formation

Unlike these other games, however, where budget spending resulted in parametric shifts which in turn caused locational adaptations; in URBAN POLITICS, players remained associated with the same cells throughout the game play. Specifically, each community player was assigned a portion of the game board to represent. He earned "success points" of 1, 5, or 10 units for each budget chip (of a designated type) placed in his area of the board. In addition, some community players had hidden, personal objectives to achieve which yielded additional "success points" to them.

The politicians in the game had dual objectives of 1) obtaining as many votes as possible and 2) achieving a hidden goal which yielded additional "success points." These hidden goals were designed so that the various politicians quickly established themselves as liberals, radicals, or conservatives. During elections, 100 votes were at stake. The number of votes received by a given politician determined his relative power during the subsequent budget allocation period. A budget of 75 millobucks (chips) was authorized each round; it took a minimum of 60 votes by the politicians acting as a body to spend all or part of the budget. Since no single politician could usually obtain 60 votes himself, coalition-formation became mandatory.

Both the type of budget chip and the specific location on the game board had to be agreed upon before the budget could be spent. A severe time constraint (15 minutes) was placed on the budget allocation period to increase pressure. The types of budget options included:

1) physical improvement
2) recreation and culture
3) housing
4) crime reduction
5) transportation
6) job creation and training
7) education
8) health and social services

Power was distributed as follows: low income (35 votes), economic interests (35 votes), middle income (25 votes), and upper income (15 votes). However, while a single player represented each of the latter three roles, seven players were assigned various parts of the low income areas and the total power distributed equally among them (5 votes each). Thus, no individual low income player had much power when compared with the middle and upper income and economic players. Accordingly, the low income players had to learn to operate as a voting bloc to swing budget allocations to their areas. However, their hidden personal objectives were designed in such a way to frustrate attempts at broad coalitions.

GAME DESIGN

URBAN POLITICS was set up around a game board color coded to depict the dominant land use in each of its 100 cells. Four land uses were represented: low income residential, middle income residential, upper income residential and commercial. The overall pattern resembled that of a typical urban area (in this case, Washington, D.C. and northern suburbs). The board layout is depicted on the next page (Figure 71).

The game, as designed, included 15 players. They were assigned roles as follows:

7 – low income representatives
1 – economic interests representative
1 – middle income representative   10 community players
1 – upper income representative
5 – politicians

Each of the 10 community players was assigned a section of the game board to represent as depicted in the game board layout. His objective was to have as much budget spending as possible occur within his assigned area. There were eight possible items on which the budget could be spent (these are listed above under Summary). Each player had a high priority budget item which he sought for his area which yielded to him 10 success points per budget chip, and a second priority budget item which yielded to him 5 success points per budget chip. Other budget

108

Figure 71

	1	2	3	4	5	6	7	8	9	10
A	U	E	E	M	U	U	U	U	M	M
B	U	E	E	M	M	M	E	E	M	M
C	U	U	M	U	U	M	E	M	M	M
D	M	M	M	U	M	M	M	M	L4,5	M
E	M	M	M	U	M	M	L4,5	L4,5	L4,5	M
F	U	M	M	E	M	L3	L3	L3	L3	M
G	U	E	U	E	E	E	E	L6	L6	L7
H	U	E	U	M	E	E	E	E	L6	L7
I	M	E	E	M	M	E	E	L6	L6	L7
J	M	E	M	M	L1,2	L1,2	M	M	M	L7

GAME BOARD LAYOUT

U = upper income
M = middle income
E = economic
L = low income
L3 = low income cells assigned to player #3

chips spent in his area yielded 1 success point per chip. (The budget chips were color-coded for easy identification by type).

In addition, some community players had hidden, personal objectives to achieve during the course of the game play. For example, low income player no. 5 was attempting to convince his fellow low income players to "riot" (see description of the riot option below). The upper income player was against any transportation spending in his part of the game board. Specific role assignments are presented at the end of the discussion of the game (Figures 76 through 90).

Each community player had a certain amount of political influence, in the form of votes, which he could use to seek demands from the politicians. The power was distributed as follows:

role	power per player	number of players	total power
low income	5	7	35
middle income	25	1	25
upper income	15	1	15
economic	25	1	25
			100

Thus, while the low income group collectively controlled the most political influence, this power was scattered among seven players. The need for coalitions quickly became evident to the low income players, although such attempts were somewhat frustrated by resultant coalitions among the more powerful three players representing the middle and upper income and economic interests.

Three election periods constituted the game. Each period began with community players stating their demands. This was followed by political speeches by each of the five politicians. Voting then occurred. Players could cast their allocated votes to any one or more politicians. Thus, for example, the economic player could cast 15 votes for politician one and 10 votes for politician five.

Low income players had an additional option. If they felt that the politicians were not responding adequately to their demands, they could cast all or part of their 5 votes in the "riot box." Thus, for example, a low income player might cast 3 votes for politician two and cast his remaining 2 votes in the "riot box." The "riot box" thus served as a numerical measure of political unrest among the low income group. Votes accumulated in the "riot box" from election to election. When 30 votes or more had accumulated, a "riot" occurred. The result was that the budget allocation for the following period was cut dramatically from 75 millobucks (chips) to 40 millobucks.

The five politicians vied for the votes of the community players. With these votes as power, they in turn attempted to spend their allocated 75 millobucks budget within a 15 minute time period. In order to spend a budget chip, or a block of chips, a specific budget action had to be put forth naming the cell or cells to receive the chip(s) and the specific type or types of chips involved. Voting then occurred on the proposed budget action among the five politicians. They could use all or part of their votes in favor of the proposed action. Thus, for example, if politician four had received 25 votes during the general election from the community players, he was free to cast up to 25 votes for any budget proposal. Clearly, if he was against the proposal he could cast 0 votes. A total of 60 or more votes was needed for approval of any proposal. (Thus, in the rare instance where a single politician received 60 or more votes during the general election, he was free

110

to act as a "dictator" and spend the budget as he pleased. More commonly, coalitions were formed among the politicians representing 60 or more votes and an overall budget was worked out by them).

In addition to attempting to win as many votes as possible during the three elections, each politician had a hidden agenda to achieve. For example, politician four wanted to see a large scale transportation system built in the city. Politician two was a "law and order" candidate, who attempted to spend as much of the budget as possible on crime reduction chips. Politician three was a "new left" candidate whose role was to frustrate the attempts of the other politicians to spend the budget.

The game play was divided into three identical election periods, each including community demands, campaign speeches, voting and budget spending. The game lasted roughly 45 minutes per period, or just over two hours in total. Score sheets utilized during the game are presented immediately following the discussion (Figures 72 through 75).

Figure 72

COMMUNITY PLAYER VOTING FORM	Role_____ Power_____	
YEAR	DEMANDS ON POLITICIANS	VOTES:
1		Politician 1_____ Politician 2_____ Politician 3_____ Politician 4_____ Politician 5_____ Riot Box_____
2		Politician 1_____ Politician 2_____ Politician 3_____ Politician 4_____ Politician 5_____ Riot Box_____
3		Politician 1_____ Politician 2_____ Politician 3_____ Politician 4_____ Politician 5_____ Riot Box_____

Figure 73

COMMUNITY PLAYER SCORE SHEET			
YEAR	POINTS EARNED FOR CHIPS	ADDITIONAL POINTS	TOTAL POINTS
1			
2			
3			
TOTAL POINTS EARNED			

DISCUSSION

The play of URBAN POLITICS was lively, and the players easily got entrenched in their roles. Tape recordings of the game play sounded remarkably like a community meeting. The game was played on several occasions: with university students, junior high school students, professional planners, and low income neighborhood groups. In each case, the game was well received and well played.

The most interesting aspect of the game is the formation of power blocs among the various community players and among the politicians. Because of the disproportionate number of low income roles (7 of 10) among the community players and their corresponding ability to consume most of the time allocated for community demands, it was particularly interesting to note the budget spending

Figure 74

POLITICAL PLAYER ELECTION RECORD			
YEAR	NOTES ON DEMANDS OF COMMUNITY PLAYERS	PLATFORM AS READ TO COMMUNITY PLAYERS	POWER RECEIVED
1			
2			
3			
		TOTAL POWER RECEIVED	

bias in favor of low income areas of the board despite their controlling only 35 percent of the total political influence.

Few players were able to "stand back" and analyze the power distribution and its implications in the early periods. However, as play progressed, power coalitions became increasingly more sophisticated as well as more consistent with actual influence wielded.

The actual running of the game is a bit more difficult than the early games described because of the high level of excitement generated among the players and the consequent activity which is in turn generated. However, there is no particularly difficult aspect other than maintaining the game flow so as to keep within the time limits allotted.

Figure 75

POLITICAL PLAYER SCORE SHEET			
YEAR	POWER UNITS RECEIVED	OTHER "SUCCESS" POINTS	TOTAL POINTS
1			
2			
3			
TOTAL			

114

15 PLAYER ROLES

(Figures 76 through 90)

Figure 76

Player Role

ECONOMIC PLAYER

You are the representative of the economic interests of the city which have establishments in the red squares of the game board. You are primarily interested in physical improvement of the economic areas (better lighting, tree planting and building repairs), and secondly, in improved transportation in these same economic areas.

As far as the game is concerned, you receive points for the following:

10 . . . . . . for every Red chip (physical improvement) located in a red square on the game board

5 . . . . . . for every Blue chip (transportation) located in a red square on the game board.

You stand to lose considerably from a riot and must attempt to convince the lower income people not to riot and the politicians to spend enough money in the lower income areas so that a riot will not take place. If a riot occurs, you lose 50 points.

Figure 77

Player Role

UPPER INCOME PLAYER

You are the representative of the upper income population of the city which lives in the light green squares on the game board. You are interested in having recreational and cultural areas developed in all the upper income portions of the board.

As far as the game is concerned, you receive five points for every green square on the game board which contains at least two recreation and cultural chips (red with green spot).

You are against any transportation system going through any of the upper income areas. You lose two points for every transportation chip (blue) located in a green square during the course of the game.

Finally, you are for manpower training programs and job opportunity creation for the poor. You receive one point for every blue chip with a green dot (job creation and training) located in the low income areas of the game board.

Figure 78

Player Role

MIDDLE INCOME PLAYER

You are the representative of the middle income population of the city which lives in the yellow squares on the game board. You are primarily interested in having additional funds spent in your areas of the game board for increased efforts to reduce crime, and secondly, for better transportation. All other improvements are, of course, welcome.

As far as the game is concerned, you receive points for the following:

10 . . . . . . for every White chip with a Green dot (crime reduction) located on a yellow square

5 . . . . . . for every Blue chip (transportation) located in a yellow square

1 . . . . . . for all other types of chips located in a yellow square.

Figure 79

Player Role

LOWER INCOME PLAYER #1

You are a representative of the lower income population which resides in squares J5 and J6 of the game board. You are primarily interested in having additional funds spent in your area for better schools, and secondly for better housing. All other improvements are, of course, welcome.

As far as the game is concerned, you receive points for the following:

10 . . . . . . for every Yellow chip (education) located in J5 or J6

5 . . . . . . for every White chip (housing) located in J5 or J6

1 . . . . . . for every other type of chip located in J5 or J6.

116

Figure 80

Player Role

LOWER INCOME PLAYER #2

You are a representative of the lower income population of the city which resides in squares J5 or J6. You are primarily interested in having additional funds spent in your area of the game board for increased job opportunities, and secondly for improved public transportation. All other improvements are, of course, welcome.

As far as the game is concerned, you receive points for the following:

10 . . . . . . for every Blue chip with a Green dot (job creation and training) located in J5 and J6

5 . . . . . . for every Blue chip (transportation) located in J5 and J6

1 . . . . . . for all other types of chips located in J5 and J6.

Figure 81

Player Role

LOWER INCOME PLAYER #3

You are the representative of the lower income population which lives in squares F6, F7, F8 and F9. You are primarily interested in having additional funds spent in your area of the game board for increased job opportunities, and secondly for better housing. All other improvements are of course welcome.

As far as the game is concerned, you receive points for the following:

10 . . . . . . for every Blue chip with a Green dot (job creation and training) located in F6, F7, F8 or F9

5 . . . . . . for every White chip (housing) located in F6, F7, F8 or F9

1 . . . . . . for all other types of chips located in F6, F7, F8 or F9.

Figure 82

Player Role

LOWER INCOME PLAYER #4

You are a representative of the lower income population which lives in squares E7, E8, E9 and D9. You are primarily interested in having additional funds spent in your area of the game board for improved public transportation service, and secondly for increased job opportunities. All other improvements are, of course, welcome.

As far as the game is concerned, you receive points for the following:

10 . . . . . . for every Blue chip (transportation) located in E7, E8, E9 and D9

5 . . . . . . for every Blue chip with a Green dot (job creation and training) located in E7, E8, E9 and D9

1 . . . . . . for all other types of chips located in E7, E8, E9 and D9.

Figure 83

Player Role

LOWER INCOME PLAYER #5

You are a representative of the lower income population which lives in squares E7, E8, E9 and D9. You are a leader of the radical element of the population. You are disgusted with the political process and feel that a riot is necessary to shake things up. Your role in the game is to convince your fellow lower income players that they should cast their votes into the riot box.

As far as the game is concerned, you receive 2 points for every vote—other than yours—which is placed in the riot box during the elections.

118

Figure 84

Player Role

LOWER INCOME PLAYER #6

You are the representative of the lower income population which lives in squares G8, G9, H9, I8, and I9. You are primarily interested in having additional funds spent in your area of the game board for better schools, and secondly for increased job opportunities. All other improvements are, of course, welcome.

As far as the game is concerned, you receive points for the following:

10 . . . . . . for every Yellow chip (education) located in G8, G9, H9, I8, or I9

5 . . . . . . for every Blue chip with a Green dot (job creation and training) located in G8, G9, H9, I8 or I9

1 . . . . . . for all other types of chips located in G8, G9, H9, I8 or I9.

Figure 85

Player Role

LOWER INCOME PLAYER #7

You are the representative of the lower income population which resides in squares G10, H10, I10, and J10. You are primarily interested in having additional funds spent in your area of the game board for increased job opportunities, and secondly for better transportation services. All other improvements are, of course, welcome.

As far as the game is concerned, you receive points for the following:

10 . . . . . . for every Blue chip with a Green dot (job creation and training) located in G10, H10, I10, and J10

5 . . . . . . for every Blue chip (transportation) located in G10, H10, I10, and J10

1 . . . . . . for all other types of chips located in G10, H10, I10 and J10.

Figure 86

Player Role

POLITICIAN #1

You are Politician One. You are interested in obtaining as much power as possible during the course of the game. For each unit of power you receive in the election, you receive one success point.

You feel that the city budget should be spent on improving housing conditions and job opportunities in the lower income areas. You receive one success point for each millobuck of the budget spent on housing (white chips) and job creation (blue chips with green dots) in the low income areas during the course of the game.

Figure 87

Player Roles

POLITICIAN #2

You are Politician Two. You are interested in obtaining as much power as possible during the course of the game. For each unit of power you receive in the elections, you receive one success point.

You are a strong supporter of law and order. You receive one additional success point for every crime prevention chip (white with green spot) placed on the game board during the course of the game.

You feel that additional money needs to be spent on transportation in the city and you gain one success point for any transportation chip (blue) placed on the game board during the course of the game.

120

Figure 88

Player Role

POLITICIAN #3

You are Politician Three. You are interested in obtaining as much power as possible during the course of the game. For each unit of power you receive in the elections, you receive one success point.

You are a radical of the new left. You enjoy creating chaos in political systems. You receive two success points for each millobuck *not* spent during the budget year, but lose one success point for every millobuck spent.

Furthermore, you gain 50 success points if a "riot" occurs.

Hint. The longer you keep your strategy and philosophy a secret, the better you will do in the game.

Figure 89

Player Role

POLITICIAN #4

You are Politician Four. You are interested in obtaining as much power as possible during the course of the game. For each unit of power you receive in the elections, you receive one success point.

You are interested in establishing a large-scale transportation system (subway) in the city. You receive 75 success points if a transportation system is built during the course of the game which connects 25 squares of the game board and has *at least two* transportation chips (blue) in each of these 25 squares.

You also favor expenditures for increased job opportunities in the lower income areas. You receive one success point for each Blue chip with a Green dot (job creation and training) spent in low income areas of the game board.

Figure 90

Player Role

POLITICIAN #5

You are Politician Five. You are interested in obtaining as much power as possible during the course of the game. For each unit of power you receive in the elections, you receive one success point.

You are chairman of the citizens' beautification program and feel that urban beautification and open space projects are most important to any city's well-being. In terms of the game, you receive one success point for every Red chip (physical improvement) and Red chip with a Green dot (recreation and culture) placed on the game board during the course of the game.

---

(5) WELFARE:

A simulation of the life of a welfare recipient

BACKGROUND

The notion of equality is a deceptive one indeed. While the American ideology is founded on a belief that "all men are created equal," most Americans know full well that all citizens do not enjoy equal rights nor have access to equal opportunities. While there are vast cultural differences within the nation, it is implicitly assumed by many that everyone has basically the same options and value systems governing these options. Perhaps the most striking case in point is that of the welfare recipient. Many Americans—perhaps a majority—sincerely believe that welfare recipients are "shiftless," "unmotivated," "exploiters," and/or "taking it easy at the expense of the taxpayer." Yet few have any real notion of what it's like to be a welfare recipient operating in the urban ghetto.

WELFARE is a crude attempt to simulate the range of events in the daily life of a ghetto dweller on welfare. It was originally designed by Bob Moore and Judy Bremner for a course conducted by the author at Howard University. It has since been modified by the author for presentation here.

SUMMARY

WELFARE is a poor man's version of MONOPOLY, the popular parlor game. A simplified board is used containing 14 positions. The players work their way around

122

the board landing randomly (based on the roll of a die) in squares marked "Landlord," "Agency," and "Hustler." They must then draw a corresponding card and face the consequences. These include immediate wins and losses or more commonly, a chance to pit their wits against the person playing the role of landlord, bureaucrat, or hustler.

The main difference between WELFARE and MONOPOLY is the use of role playing to simulate encounters between the board players and one of the three key actors (landlord, bureaucrat, and hustler). These encounters consist of three minute negotiation periods during which the player and the actor attempt to consummate a deal. These deals might include, for example, a chance to buy a "hot" bedroom set from the hustler; or a negotiation with the bureaucrat over the amount of relocation expenses to be received; or a demand on the landlord for money to repair an apartment. Other board features include a chance to "play the numbers," a wild card square with a variety of payoffs and the "jail square" common to MONOPOLY.

The object of the game for the players is to survive three circuits around the game board with the funds initially allotted as the monthly welfare payment.

GAME DESIGN

The play of WELFARE focuses on movement around the game board, depicted on the next page (Figure 91). Rules are as follows:

1. Each board player starts with a $400 welfare payment. However, he must immediately return $300 to the bank to cover shelter and food expenses. This leaves $100. With this cash allotment, the player must attempt to complete three circuits around the game board.

2. Each round a single die is thrown. The player moves the appropriate number of squares in a clockwise direction. The square in which he lands dictates his next option.

3. If a player lands in a square marked "Landlord," "Agency," or "Hustler," he must draw a card from the appropriately marked deck. Some cards will result in an immediate payoff. Others will require negotiation with the corresponding actor. The results of the negotiation will determine the payoff (see discussion of rules governing negotiations below).

4. If a player lands in the square marked "Wild Card," he must draw a card from the appropriately marked deck. A payoff will result.

5. If a player lands in the square marked "Jail," he must pay $25 to get out.

6. Each time the player passes "Start" (including the opening move of the game), he has the option of putting all or part of his money remaining on "the numbers." If he lands exactly in the square marked "Hit the "Numbers" on that same circuit, he collects four times his wager from the bank. Otherwise his money is lost.

7. Rules governing negotiations: Both the player and the actor are given a card stating their starting position for the negotiation (say, the player begins at $50 and the hustler at $500, the goal being to arrive at an agreeable sales

Figure 91

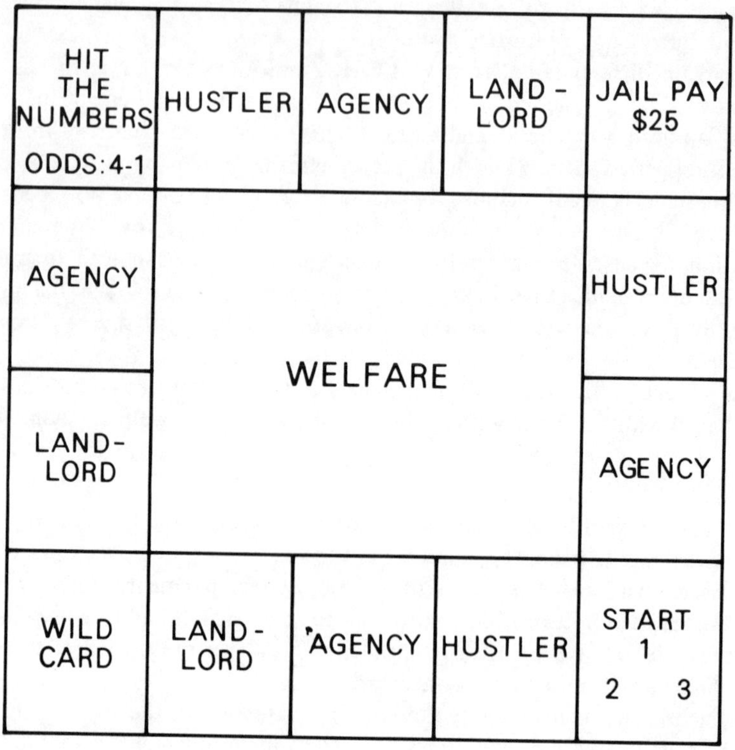

GAME BOARD LAYOUT

price for a living-room set). They have three minutes to agree on a dollar figure. Otherwise they must each pay $20 to the bank as a penalty. Before the negotiation begins, each player secretly rolls two dice, obtaining a score between "2" and "12". He receives that number of points automatically upon reaching an agreement. In addition, points ranging from "0" to "10" are given to each player upon reaching an agreement based upon the quality of their respective bargain. (Thus, for example, if the livingroom set is sold for $150, the hustler might receive "3" and the player "7".) The points earned both from the roll of the dice and for the quality of the deal are totalled. The participant with the highest total is declared the winner and receives as a payoff ten times the difference in dollars from the loser. (Thus, if the hustler had rolled an "11" and the player a "3," and the quality of the deal gave the hustler "3" and the player "7," then the hustler was the winner by a score of "14" to "10." He would thus collect $40 from the player). The roll of the dice before the negotiation was introduced to simulate the relative desires of the two negotiators to consummate a deal. The points assigned based on the quality of the deal were predetermined by the game designer based upon incremental shifts in the dollar value.

8. Should more than one player survive three circuits around the game board, the one with the highest dollar total is declared the winner. Should none survive, the last remaining player is declared the winner.

9. Each of the three actors (landlord, bureaucrat, and hustler) begins with $500. The actor with the most money at the end is declared the winner among the three.

A list of cards utilized in the play of WELFARE follows:

Agency Cards

1. Negotiation: must be relocated—try to get as much as possible from Relocation Agency. Start at $500.
2. Participate in hospital research project. Collect $20.
3. Welfare worker discovers your cheating on claims. Pay $50 hush money.
4. Receive second hand clothes. No gain or loss.
5. Long wait in clinic for treatment. Move back 5 spaces.
6. Child suffering from lead poisoning. Pay $20 for treatments.

Landlord Cards

1. Negotiation: want to rent apartment as cheaply as possible. Start at $80/month.
2. Your apartment is unsafe. Pay $50 for locks and window bars.
3. Negotiation: want to repair your house—try to get as much money as possible from landlord. Start at $300.
4. You have been active in a tenant organization. Landlord raises your rent by $20 each month.
5. You have been evicted. Pay $20 expenses looking for new apartment.
6. Landlord convicted of housing violation—you receive $100.

Wild Cards

1. Preventive detention—if you land in jail, pay $100 bail.
2. Chance of a lifetime!!! If you want, gamble all your money on one roll of a die: if you get 1, 2, 3, 4—lose all; if you get 5, 6—double your money.
3. Food stamps program—you get $50 each month to help pay for food bill beginning next month.

4. Increased welfare benefits. Monthly welfare check increased by $50 each month beginning with next check.
5. New family assistance program. Roll die, if you get a 1, 2, or 3 collect $50 extra each month. If you get a 4, 5 or 6, collect nothing extra.

Hustler Cards

1. Do hustler a favor—earn $25.
2. Negotiation: chance to get part-time job taking numbers over the phone. Try to get highest salary possible. Start by asking for $75/week.
3. Negotiation: chance to buy a "hot" living room set (worth $450)—try to get it as cheaply as possible. Begin at $75.
4. Negotiation: need $50 loan to pay off numbers man. Try to get lowest interest rate, start at 5% ($52.50 total).
5. Pay $100 repair bill on "new" television bought from hustler last month.
6. Pay $20 repair bill on "new" washing machine bought from hustler last week.

Instructions to the three actors were as follows:

Hustler

1. "Hot" living room set is worth $450. Try to get as much as you can for it. Start at $350.
2. In giving $50 loan, try to get as high an interest rate as possible. Start at 50% ($75 total).
3. In hiring part-time employee, don't pay more than $50. Try to get employee as cheaply as possible. Start at $20/week.

Agency

1. In dealing with relocatees, offer them as little as possible. Start at $100 for all moving expenses.

Landlord

1. When tenants come for money for house repairs, offer as little as possible. Start at $25.
2. When renting an apartment, try to get as much as possible. Start at $200/month.

DISCUSSION

WELFARE is a lot of fun to play. Try it. Don't be surprised if you soon find yourself playing the numbers. You should also improve your ability to deal with hustlers and bureaucrats alike. (Note: blacks play this game better than whites do. A racially mixed group is both entertaining and informative.)